Determinants
of Infant Behaviour
II

Contributing Authors

MARY AINSWORTH

J. A. AMBROSE

H. F. HARLOW

R. A. HINDE

H. F. R. PRECHTL

HARRIETT RHEINGOLD

THELMA ROWELL

H. R. SCHAFFER

J. D. SUTHERLAND

PETER WOLFF

Determinants
of Infant Behaviour II

PROCEEDINGS
OF THE SECOND TAVISTOCK SEMINAR
ON MOTHER-INFANT INTERACTION
HELD UNDER THE AUSPICES
OF THE CIBA FOUNDATION AT THE HOUSE
OF THE ROYAL SOCIETY OF MEDICINE
LONDON SEPTEMBER 1961

Edited by B. M. Foss

with a Foreword by John Bowlby

LONDON: METHUEN & CO LTD
NEW YORK: JOHN WILEY & SONS INC

First published 1963
© *1963 by Tavistock Institute of Human Relations*
Printed in Great Britain by
Butler & Tanner Ltd, The Selwood Printing Works, Frome
Catalogue No. 2/2708/10

Contents

Members of the Seminar, September 1961   viii

Editor's Note   x

Foreword by John Bowlby   xi

PART I   ANIMAL STUDIES

Harry F. Harlow: The Maternal Affectional System   3
Discussion   29

Thelma Rowell: The Social Development of Some Rhesus
   Monkeys   35
Discussion   45

PART II   HUMAN STUDIES

H. F. R. Prechtl: The Mother-Child Interaction in Babies with
   Minimal Brain Damage   53
Discussion   59

Mary Ainsworth: The Development of Infant-Mother Interaction among the Ganda   67
Discussion   104

Peter Wolff: Observations on the Early Development of
   Smiling   113
Discussion   134

Peter Wolff: The Natural History of a Family   139
Discussion   160

Contents

PART III   METHOD AND THEORY

Harriet Rheingold: Controlling the Infant's Exploratory Behaviour (*short contribution*)   171
Discussion   175

H. R. Schaffer: Some Issues for Research in the Study of Attachment Behaviour   179
Discussion   197

J. A. Ambrose: The Concept of a Critical Period for the Development of Social Responsiveness   201
R. A. Hinde: The Nature of Imprinting (*short contribution*)   227
Discussion   230

J. D. Sutherland: The Concepts of Imprinting and Critical Period from a Psycho-analytic Viewpoint (*short contribution*)   235

References   241

Index   245

Plates

facing page

1 Mother deviling by other infants 28
2 Together-together monkeys 28
3 Infant rejection by unmothered-mother 28
4 Lois nursing Elaine 28
5 Lois with aunt 28
6 Priscilla crouching over baby 28
7 Exploration forbidden: other females watch 28
8 Nursery mothers stay together 28
9a-d The rooting response 52
10 The sucking response 53
11 The grasping response 53
12a-c Changing behavioural states 60
13a, b Smiling response in 9-day-old infant 60
14 Moro response 60
15, 16 Ganda children 61, 68
17 Premature baby asleep 69
18 Premature baby with intestinal atresia 148
19 Premature baby asleep 148
20 The social smile 149
21 Eye-to-eye contact 149
22 Pat-a-cake causing laughter 149
23 Infant fed by method of propping 164
24 Studying the infant's operant behaviour 165

Members of the Seminar

Members

DR J. A. AMBROSE, Senior Psychologist, Psychoanalyst, Tavistock Child Development Research Unit: London.

MLLE G. APPELL, Psychologist, Association pour le Développement de l'Assistance aux Malades, Montrouge, Paris.

MRS MARION BERNSTEIN, Assistant Psychologist, Tavistock Child Development Research Unit, London.

DR J. BOWLBY, Consultant Psychiatrist, Director, Tavistock Child Development Research Unit; Director, Department of Children & Parents, Tavistock Clinic, London.

DR MYRIAM DAVID, Child Psychiatrist, Paris.

MR B. M. FOSS, Lecturer, Dept. of Psychology, Birkbeck College, London.

DR J. L. GEWIRTZ, Psychologist, National Institute of Mental Health, Bethesda, U.S.A.

DR MAVIS GUNTHER, Obstetrician, University College Hospital, London.

DR H. F. HARLOW, Professor of Psychology, University of Wisconsin, U.S.A.

DR R. A. HINDE, Zoologist; Curator, Field Station for the Study of Animal Behaviour, University of Cambridge.

DR E. P. G. MICHELL, Consultant Psychiatrist, Tavistock Clinic, London.

DR H. F. R. PRECHTL, Neuro-physiologist, Academisch Ziekenhuis, Groningen, Holland.

DR HARRIETT RHEINGOLD, Psychologist, National Institute of Mental Health, Bethesda, U.S.A.

MR J. ROBERTSON, Psychoanalyst, Project Officer, Tavistock Child Development Research Unit, London.

DR THELMA ROWELL, Zoologist, Sub-department of Animal Behaviour, University of Cambridge.

DR J. D. SUTHERLAND, Consultant Psychiatrist, Director, Tavistock Clinic, London.

MISS RUTH THOMAS, Psychoanalyst, Hampstead Child-Therapy Clinic, London.

DR P. WOLFF, Psychiatrist, Judge Baker Guidance Centre, Boston, U.S.A.

Members of the Seminar

Guests

DR MARY AINSWORTH, Professor of Psychology, Johns Hopkins University, U.S.A.

DR KO BEINTEMA, Neurologist, Academisch Ziekenhuis, Groningen, Holland.

MR H. R. SCHAFFER, Psychologist, Royal Hospital for Sick Children, Glasgow.

Editor's Note

For purposes of publication, the papers and contributions have been put in a different order and arranged in three sections, and the authors have revised their papers, in some cases considerably, since the meeting in September 1961. An editor finds it difficult to demur when, for instance, Dr Prechtl says in a covering letter 'as you will see, we have collected additional data which have startled us a lot, although they are still preliminary'.

The 'contributions' were mainly impromptu, but are given prominence since they formed the bases of discussion. The discussions have been reduced to roughly one-tenth of the original volume, and the selection must at times be unrepresentative. For this I apologize to the contributors. Some members of the seminar could not attend all the sessions and may as a result appear unexpectedly silent.

My thanks go to Miss Audrey Sanders, who was in charge of transcribing the recordings, and Miss Pat Willard, who looked after the correspondence and typing, for their efficiency and patience. And the group extends its warm thanks to John Bowlby for his exemplary leadership and his ability to entertain many points of view.

B. M. F.

Foreword

The convener and chairman of a seminar that meets at regular intervals is like the producer of a repertory theatre, especially one who produces repertory revue. Though each production is different, the players remain the same and the company comes to have its own distinctive character. The ingredients of each programme, moreover, have a recognizable resemblance to their predecessors, agreeable perhaps to fans, less so to critics.

After a two-year interval members of the Tavistock Seminar on Mother-Infant Interaction met for a second time in September 1961. On this occasion we were without three members of the original cast (Blauvelt, Hunter and Rosenblatt) but were joined by four others (Ainsworth, Ko Beintema, Schaffer and Wolff). The programme included new 'sketches' by some of our established members and maiden pieces from Ainsworth, Rowell, Schaffer and Wolff.

Once again priority was given to empirical studies, especially those that utilize first-hand observations of what actually happens between infant and mother. In the past these have been scarce, but an increasing number of investigators are now awakening to their interest and value, and appropriate methods and concepts are being developed. It is the hope of all the members of the seminar that the papers and discussions contained in these volumes will encourage others to embark on this time-consuming but rewarding task.

At its first meeting the group had concentrated especially on the behaviour of the neonate to the partial exclusion both of older children and of maternal behaviour. At its second meeting, attention still tended to be concentrated on the first year of life, but this time far more was given to maternal behaviour and so to interaction between infant and mother, which is our goal. The two studies using monkeys as subjects and studies of humans in Europe, Africa and America all show this trend. This is a step forward.

Once again I wish to record our thanks to the Ciba Foundation for so generously giving hospitality to participants and for other support for the meeting; and to Brian Foss for editing the proceedings. We are grateful also to those bodies which support the work of the Tavistock Child Development Research Unit. These are—the National Health Service, the Foundations' Fund for Research in Psychiatry and the Ford Foundation.

JOHN BOWLBY

PART I

Animal Studies

The Maternal Affectional System

HARRY F. HARLOW

In earlier publications we have presented the thesis that there are five primary, separable affectional systems in primates: the affection of the infant for the mother, the infant-mother affectional system; the affection of infants and children for other infants and children, the infant-infant or child-child or peer affectional system; the affection of the mother for her offspring, the mother-infant affectional system; the heterosexual affectional or male-female affectional system, which is characterized by sexual interactions between adolescents or adults of opposite sexes; and finally, the adult male affection for infants, the father-infant affectional system.

It is our firm belief that each of the affectional systems develops through a series of orderly stages and that to a considerable extent each of these affectional systems is released by a family of different underlying mechanisms or variables. In this paper we are limiting ourselves to a description and analysis of maternal affectional system through which the mother relates to her own infant or infants and to other infants.

Maternal responses to own infants

A large part of our information concerning the development of the maternal affectional system has been obtained from an apparatus which we call the playpen situation (see Fig. 1). This consists of four spacious cages each housing a mother monkey and her own infant, and an adjoining, large play area divided into four compartments by hardware-cloth partitions. A small opening in each living cage affords the babies free passage at all times between cage and playpen unless restrained by their mothers. During the first half-year of life the partition between pairs of playpens was raised two hours a day, five days a week, permitting the babies to interact with each other and with either or both mothers. The behaviours of both the mothers and the infants were measured during the interaction periods by two observers who independently recorded at successive 30-sec. intervals the occurrence of a wide range of behaviours. During the second six months the infant observations were made on pairs of infants one hour a day and all four infants were allowed to interact during a second hour.

Neonatal monkeys are continuously engaged in visually, manually, and orally exploring the body of the mother and these maternally oriented behaviours decrease, possibly as a negatively accelerated

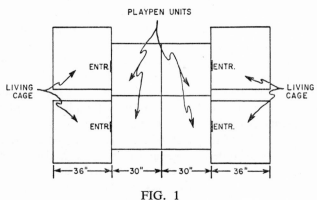

FIG. 1

Playpen situation

function, during the first 45 days of life. The neonatal monkey spends a large amount of time in oral contact with the nipples of the mother, although most of these contacts relate to non-nutritional, not nutritional, sucking. From the first few days of life onward the babies imitate their mother's behaviour in what appears to be a compulsive manner. If the mother looks at an outside object, the baby looks in the same direction; if the mother moves, the baby moves towards the same place; if a mother manipulates an object, the baby subsequently manipulates the same object. When the mother mouths and eats solid food, the baby attempts to mouth and eat solid food. Baby monkeys actually learn to eat solid food sooner when housed with their real mothers than when housed alone, and

4

this is achieved in spite of the fact that the mother actively competes with her baby for food and will snatch food from the baby's hands and even pry it out of the baby's mouth – perhaps this is where the phrase 'out of the mouths of babes' came from. These imitative behaviours increase in frequency and complexity as a positively accelerated function of time, doubtless as a function of both maturation and learning.

We believe that the maternal affectional system like the other affectional systems can be described in terms of developmental stages.

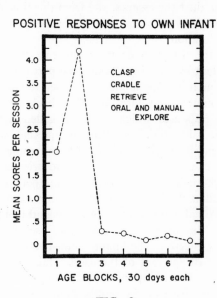

FIG. 2

We have identified three developmental stages, recognizing that these stages are characterized more by overlap in time than by complete separation. The first stage we call the stage of attachment and protection; the second, the stage of ambivalence; and the third, the stage of separation. The nature and the development of responses which characterize the first stage are shown in Fig. 2. We would argue that the first stage lasts for approximately 90 days, during which time almost all of the mother's responses to the infant are of a positive and protective nature, including such behaviours as clasping, cradling, grooming and exploring the body of the infant, frequent restraint of the infant when it attempts to leave, and rapid retrieval of the infant at the slightest threat from without.

During the first 15 to 25 days of the initial stage of maternal affection, the mother will not allow the infant to leave the living quarters despite the lure which the world outside holds for the infant. Nor is the transition easy for most mothers; they appear torn between restraining their infant and permitting it to leave the home. Gradually, as the mother's efforts to restrain weaken and the infant's efforts to explore increase, the baby escapes, and from this time onward – unless some traumatic event occurs – the baby leaves with increasing frequency and duration.

Throughout the first two or three months, the mother often retrieves her infant by reaching through the partition, grabbing her infant and pulling it into the home cage. When the infant is outside her reach, the mother may lure the infant back by either of two highly specific responses which we have called the 'affectional present' and the 'silly grin'. The affectional present, which reaches maximal frequency during the third and fourth months, appears as a full sexual present with buttocks elevated and oriented towards the infant with backwards staring through the mother's legs. The silly grin involves pulling the lips backwards without exposing the teeth and reaches maximal frequency during the second month. Although these signals for the infant's return were not used frequently, they were remarkably effective. The infants immediately returned to the mother in about 70 per cent of the cases – failure was frequently attributable to the fact that the infant was looking away from the mother instead of towards her when the mother postured.

Maternal affection and protection were also indicated throughout the first stage by constant visual orientation of the mother towards her infant and by efforts to interfere in her infant's behalf when it engaged in the joys of rough-and-tumble play with another infant. At the slightest real or implied threat, such as the experimenter's standing up at the end of a test session, the mothers rushed to the front of the cages to await their infants, which invariably rushed and clung to the appropriate mother. By the time the baby achieved separation (and probably long before), it had obviously formed a special, permanent attachment to its particular mother, and it invariably returned when disturbed or frightened to its own mother.

Thus, it has formed a specific 'the mother' attachment, not a diffuse 'a mother' or 'any mother' attachment.

The second stage, that of ambivalence, is characterized by decreasing frequency of positive responses and increasing frequency of negative responses by the mother, such as threatening, punishing, and withdrawing from her own infant. These data are presented in Fig. 3. Actually, the punishing responses may be harsh, including rough cuffing and mouthing of the infant or stiff-arming it when it

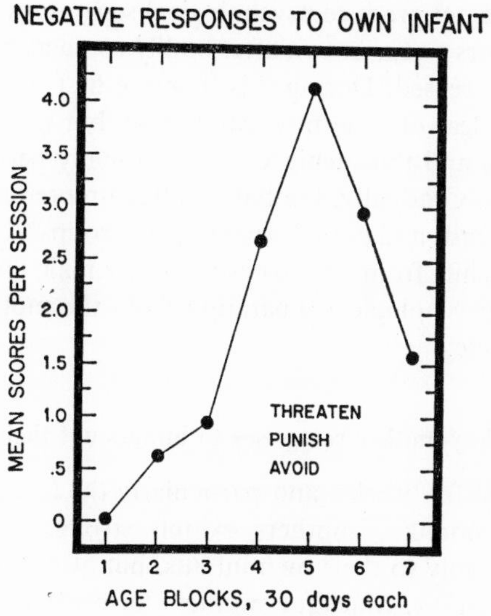

NEGATIVE RESPONSES TO OWN INFANT

THREATEN
PUNISH
AVOID

AGE BLOCKS, 30 days each

MEAN SCORES PER SESSION

FIG. 3

attempts to make contact, and many times the observers were not able to identify the external stimulus conditions which elicited these responses. This is not to be taken to mean that the mother is not still predominantly affectionate and protective; the infant still spends considerable time in close contact with the mother's body, especially at night, when it sleeps either in the mother's arms or in close contact with her body. Nevertheless, these punishing responses appear to be influential in the gradual physical separation of the infant from the mother and the development of cautious attitudes and approaches towards the mother. Indeed, the decrease in punishment scores which we see after four months (Fig. 3) probably attests to the fact that the infant learns how and when to approach a mother during this ambivalent stage of maternal affection.

The third stage is that of separation, which we have not yet studied in the laboratory. However, we have ample information concerning its nature in several species and genera of monkey from the excellent field studies which have been reported. The physical separation of the mother from its infant occurs with the birth of the next baby, and apparently this physical separation is quite traumatic for many of the babies that have been observed in the wild. Actually, physical separation does not produce psychological separation; psychological separation occurs a year or two after bodily contacts between mother and child have ceased. During this time the first baby continues to spend a great deal of time physically close, but not contacting the mother's body, and thus achieves the maximally permitted psychological identity. Gradually, the babies attach more and more intimately to the juvenile and pre-adolescent play groups. As their interests and attention shift from the mother to other male and female monkey children, psychological separation from the mother appears to become complete.

Monkey-mother responses to infants not their own

During the first few weeks, and particularly the first few days, after delivery most monkey mothers exhibit strong, diffuse maternal responses, not only to their own infants, but also to other neonatal and infant monkeys. Macaque mothers have been observed in the wild to engage in baby-snatching, robbing a less dominant mother of her own baby and raising both her infant and the other monkey infant as twins.

Actually, as is seen in Fig. 4, a group of four monkey mothers in the playpen situation showed a higher frequency of positive responses (clasping, cradling, exploring, and grooming) than negative responses (threatening, punishing, and withdrawing) to other infants entering their cages during the first 45 days. This cannot be attributed to inability to differentiate between infants, for we are certain that a special and specific attachment between each mother and her own infant has emerged well within the first month of the baby's life.

This ratio of positive to negative responses by mothers towards other infants reverses throughout all the remaining age brackets (see

8

Fig. 4). The change in direction from day 135 onwards is an artifact deriving from the infants' improving skills in avoiding punishment by mothers other than their own and from the change in some mothers from aggression to indifference towards the other infants.

Many factors may operate to account for these results. It is entirely possible that specific hormonal variables are operating to support the diffuse maternal responsiveness which characterizes the post-pregnancy period. Infant-infant interactions may be a factor in the

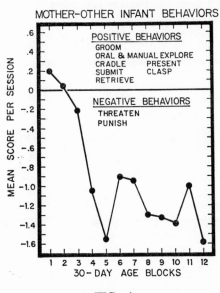

FIG. 4

reversal of the ratio of positive to negative maternal responses, for rough-and-tumble play has emerged by 45 days of age. The mothers watch the play closely and seem to begin to aggress against the other infants as the play becomes intense; perhaps the monkey mothers view the play with biased eyes. Finally, as each mother aggresses against all infants not its own, the infants come to aggress against all mothers not their own. As the ratio of positive to negative maternal responses to other infants changes, the frequency of physical contact between mothers and other infants drops rapidly to a near-zero level. This does not imply that the infants do not approach other-mothers. Actually, as is seen in Fig. 5, the absolute frequency of both approach

9

and avoidance responses increases progressively beyond the first half-year of life.

As we have already indicated the approach responses no longer involve actual physical contact with other-mothers. The infants often approach the other-mothers' cages and stay just beyond reach – usually – when the female attempts to snatch them. Or the brave infant may even threaten with face or bodily gesture and then hurriedly retreat when the mother counters in kind. The cat-and-mouse game is a favourite monkey avocation.

APPROACH VS. WITHDRAWAL RESPONSES BY
INFANTS TO MOTHERS OTHER THAN THEIR OWN

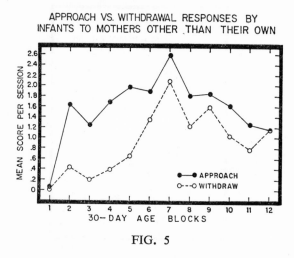

FIG. 5

Some of the more agile babies developed an even more ingenious way to devil the other-mothers. They would dash into the mother's cage and, before she could chastise them, they would rush out; one remarkable youngster would circle about the other-mother's cage, ducking and dodging as she struck out at it. Actually, this infant concentrated most of its attention on a particularly unpleasant mother that in spite of her best efforts failed to intercept it. Eventually she became exhausted with the sport and assumed an attitude of utter indifference even when the baby would lie down on the floor of the cage with face averted. The infant could not possibly then have escaped had the mother assaulted, which she never did. We might point out that the infant's response was a response typically implying submission to another monkey.

ROWELL *How old was it?*
HARLOW *Four or five months of age.*
ROWELL *Was it a grooming gesture?*
HARLOW *It could well be but the other-mother never groomed.*

Another kind of approach pattern that the infants developed towards other-mothers was that of mutual bedevilment, the most complex pattern of co-operative play that we have seen in infant monkeys. Three infants – the mother's own infant was never included – would simultaneously bedevil by approaching, taunting, and threatening an other-mother, as is seen in Plate 1. Not infrequently two of the infants would stay close together and the third separate somewhat. Then, when the mother threatened or snatched at the pair, the third would suddenly grab and pull on the mother's body even to the point of removing a handful of fur. This game was played both for fun and for keeps – and for obvious reasons has never been observed in the wild!

Comparison of behavioural effects of animate and inanimate mothering

In earlier researches designed to analyse the variables underlying the attachment and affection of the infants for mothers, we were able to demonstrate that infants developed strong attachments to inanimate cloth-surrogate mothers and that these bonds were in large part independent of nutritional support. Furthermore, at an appropriate motivational age the surrogate-mothers not only gave their infants attachment and comfort, but, surprisingly enough, imparted to them a very considerable degree of security and protection when the infants were placed in a strange or frightening situation. Even so, the best inanimate surrogate is a very unsubtle mother and it contradicts common sense to believe that any surrogate-mother can replace completely the contributions of real mothers to the later personal-social development of their infants.

The role of the real mother was measured by comparing under identical test conditions in the playpen situation the behaviours of four babies each raised on a differential cloth surrogate with the behaviours of four infant macaque monkeys each raised with its own live monkey mother.

11

The data of Fig. 6 demonstrate that the surrogate-raised infants exhibited a significantly higher level of oral exploration, both oral exploration directed to themselves and also social oral exploration directed towards playmates, during the daily two-hour period of social interaction. The differences in social oral exploration during the first 30 days were doubtless influenced by the fact that the real mothers restrained their infants early in life and limited the infants' opportunities to associate with each other and to interact. Inanimate mothers are totally passive and permissive. However, the differences in both behaviour categories continued throughout and actually

ORAL EXPLORATION

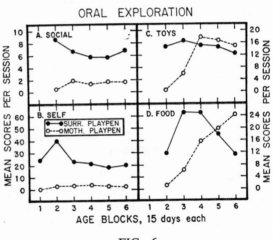

FIG. 6

beyond the 90-day test period. These data in no sense indicate that the surrogate infants operated at a higher level of socialization than the monkey-mothered infants. Nothing could be farther from the truth, for we have found in many test situations that excessive orality in monkeys is a mark of social inadequacy and infantilism.

Even during early social contacts the mother-raised babies appeared to interact more freely and subtly and have more social awareness than the surrogate-raised infants. One such behavioural aspect was that of facial expressions, which we presume the monkey-mothered infants had acquired during the course of mother-child interactions. As shown in Fig. 7, the facial threat pattern of retracting the lips, exposing the teeth, and flattening the hair on the top of the head appeared earlier in the mother-playpen infants than in the surro-gate-playpen and was maintained at a higher level during the first 200 days. Another facial pattern, that of social frowning, is relatively frequent in the mothered infants and exceedingly rare in those raised on cloth surrogates.

Our initial primary concern about the influences of differential mothering was directed towards the effects of real and inanimate mothering on the development of the various play patterns which assume an overwhelmingly important role in the determination and formation of infant-infant affectional relationships during the first

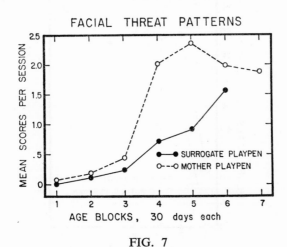

FIG. 7

year of life. As was already indicated, these behaviours were studied by permitting pairs of infants to interact freely while observed two hours a day during the first half-year of life.

Since the opportunity for play is a function of the time that the infants are out of their home cages and moving about the playpen compartments, the data for total time in the playpen are presented in Fig. 8. During the first 60 days of life the surrogate infants actually spend considerably more time in the playpen compartments than do the real-mothered monkeys simply because of frequent maternal restraint and intervention. From 90 days onwards there are no differ-ences between the two groups in total time spent in the playpen.

However, from early in life onwards the real-mothered infants show

13

superiority in social play responses over the surrogate-mothered babies both in terms of the time of appearance of the various play patterns and also in terms of the complexity of play patterns which develop during the first year of infancy. The first true play pattern is that of rough-and-tumble play, in which pairs of monkeys wrestle, roll, tug, and mouth each other with considerable vigour without any animal's ever becoming hurt or injured. As is shown in Fig. 9, within the first 60 days, as soon as the mothered infants have effected

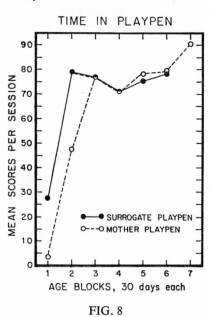

TIME IN PLAYPEN

FIG. 8

partial maternal separation, the absolute frequency of rough-and-tumble play scores is higher for the mothered monkeys than the non-mothered monkeys, and these differences become accentuated with time.

Similar, and in all probability accentuated, differences are found in initial time of onset and in the intensity of the next play pattern to develop, a pattern we call approach-withdrawal play. This is a play pattern in which actual physical contact becomes greatly reduced. It is a 'you chase me and I'll chase you pattern' in which the animals pursue each other back and forth with relatively brief interspersed

14

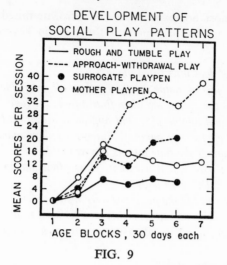

FIG. 9

bouts of physical contact. We have also referred to it as 'non-contact play'.

As the monkeys approach the end of the first year of life, the tempo of their play activities increases and they come more and more to incorporate all available objects – animate and inanimate – into a pattern of integrated play which might equally well be described as a pattern of 'mad-activity play'. As is seen in Fig. 10, this play

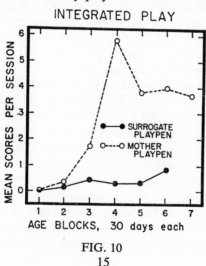

FIG. 10

15

pattern is almost non-existent in the surrogate-raised infants but becomes a vigorous play pattern for the monkey-mother-raised infants.

THOMAS *What does integrated mean?*

HARLOW *It's just a name implying that all available objects are brought into the play. Even when four infants are together and available, rough-and-tumble play and approach-withdrawal play usually involve discrete pairs of monkeys. Integrated play commonly involves all four infants if the four infants are available.*

GEWIRTZ *Just a technical question. How often did you make these observations? Every 15 days?*

HARLOW *Early in life the monkeys were tested seven days a week and then the test schedule subsequently was reduced to five days a week.*

GEWIRTZ *Every day? An observation was made on all these dimensions?*

HARLOW *Two hours a day.*

GEWIRTZ *Every slide has different dimensions. All of these were checked every day?*

HARLOW *Yes. All of these and other behavioural measures not presented here were checked every day by two experimenters observing simultaneously.*

The comparative data on the social development of the two groups of macaque infants, one raised by real, animate monkey mothers and the other raised by artificial, inanimate mother-surrogates, demonstrates clearly that the mother plays an important role in the subsequent personal-social development of her infant. Although we have no clear-cut, definitive data concerning the mechanisms by which the mother assists her infant, it does appear that early mother-infant association stimulates the formation and differentiation of facial – and probably total bodily – expressions that subsequently facilitate positive social interaction.

Furthermore, we believe that the mother provides a kind of body contact that is not provided by any surrogate-mother and that this contact facilitates the normal development of the later maturing affectional systems. The cloth surrogate provides contact, but it is essentially a passive contact which does not feed back or feeds back minimally when the infant clings. Maternal contact, on the other hand, is dynamic, and the infant becomes trained to adjust its own

16

responses to those of the mother to maintain and even attain contact comfort.

Again, the mother gives to the infant, and stimulates the infant to reciprocate, complexities of contactuality that cannot be provided by any inanimate surrogate. The mother apparently stimulates the infant by sexual presentation and genital play, and we are quite certain that the infant directs sexual responses to the real mother earlier than to the surrogate. Finally, most mothers intensively groom their infants. This is a very powerful primate form of social interacting, apparently pleasurable to both donor and recipient. It is probable that the multiple positive postural interactions between monkey mother and child impart to the infants acceptance of, and active seeking for, reciprocal physical contact with other monkey infants and that this positive contactual acceptance greatly facilitates the play patterns which underlie the formation and development of the infant-infant affectional system, our second primate affectional system.

Infant-mother deprivation

During the previous year we conducted some small pilot studies relating to mother-infant separation and we have nearly completed one formal investigation. The apparatus was for all practical purposes a half of a playpen situation, with two living cages each housing a mother and infant and two playpen compartments. Two pairs of mothers and infants were tested and were separated when the infants were approximately 170 and 200 days of age. Separation was achieved by dropping a Plexiglas partition between the living cage and playpen while the infant was outside the living area. Thus, infant and mother could see and hear each other but could not make physical contact.

Mean frequency of infant visual fixations of the mother during a one-hour observation period in the three weeks of separation and the three weeks both pre- and post-separation are given in Fig. 11. It is obvious that the number of visual fixations is significantly enhanced by separation but that this response adapts or extinguishes progressively during separation. Early in the separation phase the infant spent a large amount of time sucking its thumb and crying piteously while pressing against the Plexiglas partition near its mother. Whether or not the intensity of separation anxiety was increased or decreased by permitting visual contact must remain an open question.

Two of the four mothers exhibited an increase in visual fixations directed towards the baby, but the pattern was less persistent in the mothers than it was in the infants. We had predicted that because of its greater maturity, the mother would be more disturbed than the infant, but this prediction, made on no firm basis, did not hold.

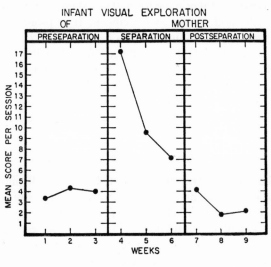

FIG. 11

AINSWORTH *How long each day would the baby be kept separated?*

HARLOW *Twenty-four hours a day throughout the three-week period. During the separation period the babies never made physical contact with the mother, though they could always see the mother.*

BOWLBY *Presumably because it is doing this, it isn't doing much else.*

GEWIRTZ *Why did you stop the deprivation after three weeks? Because it looked very much as though you had an extinction curve.*

HARLOW *Jack, we designed this as a three weeks' pre-separation, three weeks' separation, three weeks' post-separation, experiment and we followed the experimental design through.*

GEWIRTZ *The fact that the visual responses were not reinforced by contact and other things could have caused them to extinguish.*

HARLOW *Even though the visual responses are self-reinforcing, they still dropped in frequency.*

GEWIRTZ *We do not know if they are self-reinforcing. All we know is that they drop in frequency.*

HARLOW *We do not know that they are reinforced by contact either.*

GEWIRTZ *That is the interpretation I would give, of course. But then this is a different kind of separation from the usual one that we have been talking about at this conference. You usually do not have sight of the mother.*

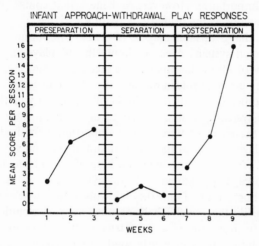

FIG. 12

HARLOW *We tried to get a situation where there would be the maximum disturbance. There had been a small study of Jensen and Tolman (1962) at the University of Washington, on separation for brief periods of time over a number of days, and the results were not very striking. We tried to get a situation where we would get maximal disturbance from separation. We arbitrarily chose this situation.*

The serious and persisting impact of maternal separation on the infants is demonstrated by the near total abolition of play responses by the infants during the separation period, as graphed in Fig. 12. Furthermore, there is no indication of any recovery or development of play throughout the three-week separation interval. It would appear that play activities recovered only gradually after separation

19

ended, but the mothers were properly apprehensive about permitting infantile separation for a considerable period of their infants' return.

Together-together infant monkeys

The most important mechanism that we have been able to find that binds the infant monkey to the mother is that of contact comfort. It is true that early in life nursing and rocking are apparently variables of measurable importance, and warmth is apparently a variable of persisting importance. However, we believe that contact or contact comfort remains as the primary, persisting variable.

The fact that a variable may be of primary importance to one of the affectional systems does not imply that it plays an equivalent role in any or all of the others. The fact that a particular variable may play an essential role in one affectional system and a destructive role in another is one of the criteria of separability of the various affectional systems. At first by chance and subsequently by design we tested the effect of unrestrained opportunity for body contact upon the development of the infant-infant affectional system.

Because of limited cage space we housed two of our infants together in a cage approximately 18 in. by 18 in. by 24 in., and in a relatively short period of time they had gone into a tight clasp pattern much more like that which a baby monkey shows to a cloth surrogate than like its responsiveness to a true monkey mother. We were impressed by the total or nearly total destructiveness of this tight-clasp, together-together pattern once it had become established.

Aside from our playpen situation we had developed another extremely effective test situation for measuring the play patterns which characterize the first year of the infant-infant affectional system. As illustrated in Fig. 13, this is a room 8 ft. high with approximately 46 sq. ft. of floor space. It contains a number of movable toys and various objects such as a rotating wheel, flying rings, an artificial tree, a climbing screen, and a ledge that enable the subjects to move freely in a three-dimensional world.

However, even this stimulating environment failed to detach the together-together pair for play together or with the two normal monkeys of similar ages also present in each playroom session. We then deliberately raised two additional pairs of together-together monkeys and tested all four in the playroom simultaneously,

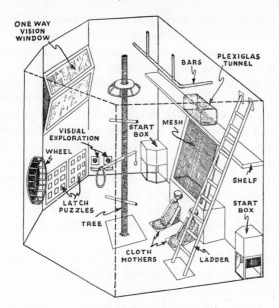

FIG. 13.

Social playroom

comparing their behaviour with that of groups of four monkeys that lived with cloth surrogates except for the daily 20-min. sessions of playroom experience.

BOWLBY *These are infants that have been brought up with their mothers up to this point?*

HARLOW *No. These were taken from their mother on day 1 – at birth – and put together when a few days of age.*

SCHAFFER *One of those monkeys was sucking its thumb while tightly clasping.*

HARLOW *Infants raised on surrogate-mothers show a very large amount of sucking – much more than infants raised on real mothers. But of course, infants raised with real mothers show a large amount of non-nutritional attachment to the breast.*

Throughout the 180 test days the together-together monkeys continued to show a high degree of orality directed towards self and partner whereas orality in the playroom situation greatly decreased in the surrogate-raised monkeys after 90 days of age.

As one might expect, the together-together monkeys exhibited an increasing amount of mutual clinging in the playroom situation, paralleling the development of the together-together pattern in the small living cage. The important point is that the playroom test sessions did not prevent the development of the together-together pattern, and within 40 days the mutual clinging pattern dominated the behaviour of the together-together monkeys even in the playroom. Conversely, mutual ventral clinging was essentially non-existent in the surrogate-raised monkeys. Finally, the together-together monkeys seldom made any attempt to initiate play either with each other or later when they were paired with the two normally playful monkeys; for all practical purposes, they never engaged in any play behaviour whatsoever.

When the together-together monkeys grow older, there is some tendency for one to cling to the back of the other as the presumably more independent or more dominant monkey moves about, but when locomotion ceases, or as soon as either one is startled, they immediately resume mutual ventral clinging.

BOWLBY *Does each have his own specific role or do they reverse roles?*
HARLOW *They do not reverse roles, at least over a long period of time. Each has his own role.*
GEWIRTZ *Has any one of these ever got old enough to mate?*
HARLOW *No. The oldest pair is only a little over a year of age now. The other two pairs are something like seven or eight months of age.*
THOMAS *There is no male-female situation involved in this?*
HARLOW *All of these animals are females because all the males born about that time were needed in other researches.*

At approximately 180 days of age we shuffled the two younger pairs of together-together monkeys, placing each of the members of the A pair with a member of the B pair for two weeks. Both new pairs immediately went into the ventral-ventral cling pattern and there was no evidence of loss, bereavement, or separation anxiety for the previous partner. After two weeks of re-pairing, all four were again brought into the playroom, and none of them showed any interest in its previous partner. A half-year of completely intimate physical attachment had produced no specific personal attachments.

22

We also have a group of four monkeys raised together in a larger cage, 6 ft. by 3 ft. by 3 ft., placed there when the oldest was about 15 days of age. These animals quickly developed a pattern characterized by mutual dorsal-ventral clinging, as illustrated in Plate 2. However, from time to time one or two of the animals would break away from the group both in the home cage and the playroom and explore and eventually engage in a slow-motion semblance of normal individual play.

BOWLBY *I take it that there are masses of evidence that infants and mothers make very close pair relationships, with individual preferences, in the first 90 days of life, yet these infants brought up together-together do not. It seems to me an extraordinary contrast. These are the facts, I take it?*

HARLOW *You are absolutely correct but I would stress that the real mother rejects as well as clings and gradually establishes psychological and social distance in the infant. Furthermore, the babies of real mothers develop specificity of infant-mother affection. We have described two playpen situations – babies with real mothers and babies with cloth-mothers – and, of course, it is not surprising at all that there is a much greater specificity of attachment of the infant with the real mother than the infant with the cloth surrogate even though the four cloth surrogates had different appearances varying in their head shape and their body colour. We did not do systematic work, but when the experimenters at the end of each test session stood up, all four babies with real mothers fled to the real mother and always attached to the real mother from very early in life. We are sure that there's a complete specificity between baby and real mother, and as early as one can measure, it is a completely specific bond. In the same situation with the cloth-mothers, the babies usually go to the right cloth-mother but not always, and not infrequently babies will go to the wrong cloth-mother or two babies will go to a single cloth-mother and three babies may all go to a single cloth-mother. So there's nothing like the specificity of maternal attachment to a mother-surrogate, even a good surrogate, as there is to a real mother. There is no question that these babies know which is their surrogate, because when frightened, between 75 per cent and 90 per cent of the time they do make the right choice, even though they have to move a fair distance around the cage to get there.*

THOMAS *It is interesting to see that they prefer the cloth-mother to each other. Would they be fed by these cloth-mothers?*

HARLOW *Yes, they are fed by the cloth-mother; all of their feed comes from the cloth-mother except for solid food. You are right. They do not cling to each other. They always go to a mother even if it is not an entirely adequate mother.*

The maternal behaviour of unmothered-mothers

We have investigations on four animals we call 'unmothered-mothers'. They are four females that never had a real mother of their own. One of them was raised on a bare wire cage and three were raised on cloth surrogates.

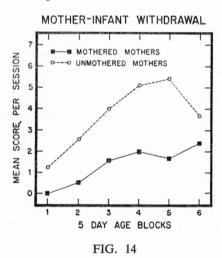

MOTHER-INFANT WITHDRAWAL

FIG. 14

Plate 3 shows one of our unmothered-mothers. Here the mother sits staring into space – while the infant makes a desperate attempt to get to her. The mother puts her hand on the infant and crushes its body into the floor of the cage. All four of these animals in their original contacts were either completely indifferent or violently abusive to their infants. No baby was ever killed. Sometimes the presence of the experimenters seemed to exaggerate the aggressive response of the mothers, so that in the case of one mother we stopped all observation for two days because we were afraid. In some cases

24

we had to take the babies out of the cage to feed them for quite a number of days.

The withdrawal of mothers from the infants is shown in Fig. 14, comparing a group of mothered-mothers and a group of unmothered-mothers. The unmothered-mothers show a great many more withdrawal responses.

The frequency of infant approaches to the mother is depicted in Fig. 15 and there is a far greater frequency of approaches by the infants to the unmothered-mothers than to the mothered-mothers. The

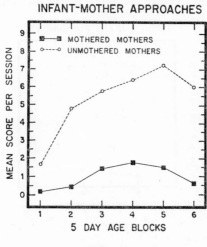

FIG. 15

answer is perfectly simple. When the infant approached the good mother, the mother accepted it and the baby did not have to approach again. One of the things that would unnerve experimenters was to watch the desperate efforts of these babies to make contact with the abnormal mother. She would beat them and knock them down; they would come back and make contact; the mothers would rub their face into the floor; they would wriggle free and again attempt contact. The power, insistence, and demandingness of the infant to make contact and the punishment the infant would accept would make strong men reach the point that they could hardly bear to observe this unmaternal behaviour.

The babies developed many ways to make contact, and a common

25

one was for the baby to make contact by getting to the back of the mother and then gradually wriggling its way to the ventral surface.

Punishment responses are graphed in Fig. 16. During the first 30 days there are practically no punishment responses by the mothered-mothers and there is a high level of punishment responses by the unmothered-mothers. The reason why the unmothered score was as low as it was lay in the fact that some mothers were just indifferent when the neonate was too young to make contact. First, the mother would simply avoid the infant and subsequently, when the infants actually struggled to make contact, a higher increase in number of

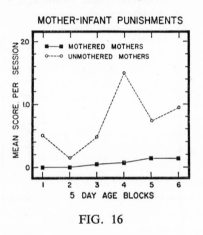

MOTHER-INFANT PUNISHMENTS

FIG. 16

punishment responses resulted. Sometimes the mother would just go over and beat the infant without any reason whatsoever.

These unmothered-mothers would show some limited indications of maternal behaviour, and there was some grooming, though rather inadequate grooming, of the infants by some unmothered-mothers.

One striking finding was the high level of visual exploration by the unmothered-mothers of the other infant. One could see them sitting, staring, looking and watching another mother's infant and paying absolutely no attention to their own. I am sure the reason why good mothers do not spend time visually exploring other infants is that they are busy visually exploring their own.

BOWLBY *Does maternal behaviour improve as time goes on?*
HARLOW *We simply do not know because the oldest of the infants had*

only been with their mothers, when I left, about 45 days. It was my impression that the behaviour was improving somewhat, but it still appeared to be grossly abnormal in all of the females. One of the females was not really so terribly abusive even early – you get individual differences – but really normal mother-infant patterns never developed.

Sex behaviour of non-mothered monkeys

We have studied the sex behaviour of the babies we separated from their mothers and then raised until they became sexually mature. We have a number of different early-experience situations. We have babies that were raised in isolated wire cages; we have a few babies that were raised on wire surrogates; and many babies raised on cloth surrogates. Also we have data on babies raised on cloth surrogates but given playroom experience. (These babies had 20 min. a day to play with other infants, but they never had anything other than a surrogate-mother.) We have babies that were raised on real mothers in the playpen situation; we have babies raised on cloth-mothers in the playpen situation. Now, in the case of the babies raised in isolated cages and those raised on cloth surrogates but never having had any opportunity to play with other infants – in other words completely denied infant-infant affectional formation – none of the males has bred in spite of every effort that we have been able to make. As far as we could make out it appears that they are heterosexually hopeless, even though they give every sign of showing normal sex development, in terms of testes biopses, and they look like adult males. Apparently all of them have been sexually destroyed and it seems to make no difference whether they were raised in isolated cages or raised with cloth surrogates for a considerable period of time.

In the case of the females in the same conditions, it was our first impression that they would be sexually hopeless. For the oldest animals, the ones raised in wire cages, we first tried breeding and we got nowhere, absolutely nowhere. Some of the younger animals were placed on an island in Madison's Vilas Park Zoo – we call it our group therapy experiment – for six weeks with our finest breeding male and he got nowhere, absolutely nowhere. However, we have continued tests, where we take these females and put them with our best breeding males – some of these breeding males are just wonderful boys, patient, sweet, gentle, unhurried, and that is where the unmothered-mothers came from. We have one female that was raised in a wire cage in isolation that became a mother and it is all due to a very wonderful male named Smiley. The other three unmothered-mothers were raised with cloth surrogates. We now think that three or four other of these females that were raised on cloth surrogates are pregnant. We had one female which failed to become pregnant in the first, what we might call successful, heterosexual session, and with this in mind she was reintroduced to the male for five or six different cycles. As far as we know she is not pregnant, but her behaviour began to change progressively and by the time of the fourth or fifth cycle she was showing normal female sexual patterns. But at least in some of these impregnation is possible even without their showing any normal sex behaviour. Some of these cloth-raised females were impregnated by simply incredible feats of motor skill on the part of the male.

It appears that in the case of the animals that were raised with real mothers in the playpen situation and also given opportunity to interact with other infants almost from birth on, that both the males' and the females' sex behaviour patterns are normal, complete and full, and if these animals do not become impregnated when adult, I would be surprised. In the case of the babies raised in the playpen situation with cloth surrogates and given ample opportunity for normal infant-infant interaction, we are not sure. Some are showing at least a semblance of normal sex posturing and behaviour. These babies raised in the playroom, even though they never had a real mother, were given a very remarkable opportunity to interact, to develop normal infant-infant affectional patterns. The males and females are apparently showing normal sex behaviour even though they are under two years of age – one should see the pattern, if it is going to appear, by then – and it is our belief that these may develop normal adolescent and adult heterosexual behaviour. (*Normal sexual behaviour subsequently was observed in all members of this group. H. H.*)

I think it becomes obvious that the likelihood of normal sex behaviour in both the male and the female is greatly facilitated by a normal mother-infant relationship, but the importance of normal interaction of infants with other infants must not be underestimated.

28

PLATE 1. Mother deviling by other infants

PLATE 2. Contactual responses by group of four together-together
monkeys

PLATE 3 (*above left*). Infant rejection by unmothered-mother
PLATE 4 (*above right*). Lois nursing Elaine. The babies turn round to watch other animals, still holding the teat in the corner of the mouth

PLATE 5. In the second week Lois would leave her baby with an aunt. Here it climbs on Rosie's back while Pris grooms her

PLATE 6 (*top*). Priscilla did not restrain the baby, but followed it everywhere, crouching over it

PLATE 7 (*middle*). Ruth held her baby back anxiously when she tried to
explore. Females in neighbouring cages took a keen interest in the interactions between mothers and babies

PLATE 8 (*bottom*). The mothers stayed together most of the time, nursing
their babies (Molly on the right, Ruth left)

Perhaps this second affectional system is even more important than the first in the development of normal heterosexuality. Of course there is an interaction between systems.

Data we hope to obtain but do not yet have are data on babies raised with real mothers but denied during the first 6 to 12 months any opportunity for infant-infant interaction. We shall see what happens to them. The results are anyone's bet. However, it is this kind of potential research that makes me think one should use great caution in interpreting the effects of mother-infant relationships or the effects of any kind of early experience, since it is obvious that the interaction of these two affectional systems – maternal and infant-infant – is very important.

Discussion following Professor Harlow's paper

HINDE *Harry, would you care to say just what you mean by a system? And what you mean when you say that systems interact?*

HARLOW *Of the variables that produce normal infant-mother affection, it seems to me that contact is the most important, though nursing is apparently a variable of measurable importance, and warmth is very obviously a variable of measurable importance. On the other hand, the infant-infant system, the second system, is simply a maturational development of a series of ever-increasingly complex play patterns, characterized not by contact but by the opposite of contact, interaction without tight clasp, which is apparently destructive to it. It looks to me as if there is something logically different between the infant-mother pattern and the infant-infant affection. But also they differ in terms of a very fundamental variable and in one case they completely reverse their roles. Thus I think there is rather good indication of the separability of these two systems. The maternal system I suspect has much in common with the infant-mother affectional system, even though we do not know all of the underlying variables. We do know that they are not the identical variables underlying the first two systems. I think that logically these are separate systems and I think that biologically they are separate systems. In the case of sex, I think that there are clearly two systems, because both in terms of sex behaviours and non-sex behaviours, they are almost completely separated early in life. Within the first six months of life, the boy monkeys romp and wrestle and the girl monkeys run. Little girls never chase little boys, little boys may chase little girls.*

FOSS *From what you have told us, the bad mothering perpetuates itself and one would expect different groups of monkeys in different countries to have different mores in this respect.*

HARLOW *Maybe they do. Different species of monkeys have different mores. We are very intrigued as to what is going to happen to these bad mothers on the next pregnancy. I think there is a high probability that they will improve.*

BOWLBY *It would be very odd if they didn't improve somewhat because, as you have already remarked, they have not only been unmothered but they have been isolated, so this is the first experience they have had with any monkey companion at all.*

AINSWORTH *It will also be interesting to see what happens to the babies of unmothered-mothers when they become mothers.*

HARLOW *All we have to do is to wait four or five years. You see, one deliberately does this to try to get long-term support! You can't hurry this research.*

FOSS *I suppose it's unfair to ask if, when these monkeys see other monkeys behaving sexually, it has any facilitating effect?*

HARLOW *I don't know. We have absolutely no data on this.*

FOSS *Even in rats it's supposed to. One would assume it would here.*

AINSWORTH *May I ask what percentage of these unmothered females did mate successfully?*

HARLOW *Well, I think we could put it this way. You see, our babies raised in wire cages and babies raised on cloth surrogates confound the factor with age. The babies raised in wire cages are older. They are around 4 to 7 years of age, so you must have for any chance of mating, very large strong males because otherwise the female dominates the male and practically she will never have anything to do with him if she can dominate him. The male runs and that ends it. We don't think – I hate to say it because every year I get crossed up – we don't think that by any technique we are going to be able to mate a high percentage of babies who were raised in the wire cages, except by artificial insemination. We now believe that in the case of these babies which were raised on the cloth-mothers and to whom we were able to give sex experience somewhat earlier, that we are going to be able to impregnate by normal means a fairly high percentage.*

We would certainly guess at least 50 per cent and it's entirely possible that we may impregnate 100 per cent of them before time runs out. The fact that they mate doesn't mean that their sex behaviour is normal. Most of it is not normal.

ROWELL *I think that was where we had a big discrepancy in age at onset of behaviour, in that my male was showing mounting and thrusting at 15 weeks and yours not until 15 months.*

HARLOW *Oh, there's no discrepancy at all. Absolutely none. You see, it's a question of normal and abnormal sex behaviour. By this period of time you see these monkeys sitting on the cloth-mother in the playroom situation and mounting and thrusting. Typically the thrusting is indiscriminate regards positioning, now at the head, they thrust at the head – most frequently they mount at the lateral side and then thrust laterally across the body surface. We have what we call a combined learning and yearning curve in this playpen situation. There is a tendency as time passes for the male to show a statistically greater increase in dorsal thrusting, but now we think – we hazard a guess – that this comes under play patterns. In the play pattern the female is passive, it flees. When it stops it frequently keeps its head averted from the male, so when the male approaches and clasps her he is automatically clasping in a ventral-dorsal position which is the position of normal mating.*

ROWELL *Yes, but there is a lot of difference in our baby rhesus when the male first mounted her. She tried to walk on, and she yawned and wriggled about, but two weeks later she would stand like a rock and act just like a female. This is the difference between 15 and 17 weeks.*

HARLOW *How old is the male?*

ROWELL *Five days younger.*

HARLOW *And they have been raised with other monkeys? I don't think we have any monkeys exhibiting normal sex behaviour at 15 weeks.*

ROWELL *This is quite ludicrously normal. They're so tiny you don't expect it. Maybe they have been learning from watching the others. I can hardly believe it but it would suggest it.*

HARLOW *If you had four cases I would buy it.[1] This is an interesting*

[1] Dr Rowell states that more recently a male has shown correctly oriented mounting and thrusting at 10 weeks, and another female presenting at about 15 weeks.

31

question. *How much of the total cultural pattern do you have to put in to get behaviour that's normal and at a normal time? We don't know.*

BOWLBY *Of course these unmothered-mothers, who were so inept and aggressive, had had no opportunity of watching other-mothers being maternal.*

HARLOW *Yes, you're right.*

BOWLBY *And it's conceivable that they might have been a little more kindly had they had such experience.*

HARLOW *Yes, indeed. Occasionally we do get a mother raised normally that is indifferent to the child, but not four out of four.*

APPELL *Did these mothers ever resent you taking away the baby?*

HARLOW *Ordinarily, no. Normally we can't take anything out of the cage, but with the first of these females we were able to take the baby away with no trouble because she was paying absolutely no attention to it; but in the case of the one that was abusive, we were able to take the baby away only with difficulty. It was easiest to baby-snatch when the mother was indifferent and made no attempt to retrieve a baby which had wandered away or which it had abandoned.*

BOWLBY *Which is very peculiar, isn't it?*

HARLOW *Very. And as a matter of fact with some of these animals we can go up and threaten both mother and child and get no response from the female, at least early after delivery.*

BOWLBY *Of course, there are very few human mothers who are anything like as bad as that. Even what is called a bad mother would hardly put up 30 per cent as bad a performance as that. They would be in prison or at least a police court.*

THOMAS *Well, there are very few mothers who have had such an infancy.*

FOSS *Is the mother who was brought up in the empty cage no different from the other three?*

HARLOW *The one brought up in the wire cage was probably the most completely indifferent, though not the most abusive mother. It was the one that showed this utter indifference, and later became somewhat abusive.*

SCHAFFER *Do you think she was mentally defective? I am raising the possibility quite seriously. I'm thinking of the degree of total deprivation.*

HARLOW *We have never run across a mentally defective monkey. We have tested hundreds of them. I think the answer is that it is conceivable that these animals are mentally defective but very unlikely.*

SCHAFFER *I was wondering if this was a Spitzian kind of thing.*

HARLOW *We have never seen any syndrome which approaches hospitalism except in the case of babies raised in total social isolation – where they never see another monkey. There is just the possibility that long periods of total or partial social deprivation produce some slight loss of learning ability, but the amazing thing is the degree to which you can isolate these animals without learning loss. Now, I know this is not like the human baby. We will take a big broad guess as to why they are different and that is I think it is possible that social isolation in the human being really does not have as serious effect on intelligence as measurements would indicate. What it does is that it destroys the capability of the infant to socialize. If the infant cannot socialize, it cannot then develop an adequate language. If it cannot develop an adequate language it is going to test at a less adequate level than its theoretical capability.*

AINSWORTH *I have come to nearly precisely the same conclusion.*

The Social Development of some Rhesus Monkeys[1]

THELMA E. ROWELL

The observations described here were made on the first three babies born in a recently established colony of Rhesus monkeys. One has been observed up to the age of 12 months, the other two to 5 months. Because the number is so small, any suggestions or conclusions must be tentative, but in the present context I hope you will find them worth discussing even at this stage.

The babies were born into two groups of animals, each living in a pen with a large outside run connected by a swing door with a smaller room indoors. Table 1 gives the names of the animals in each group, and indicates their social relationships. I shall refer to females living in the same group as a mother and baby as Aunts.

Before social interactions, other than the crudest, can be considered, it is necessary to consider what methods of communicating are available. Monkeys communicate with each other by voice, facial expression, and gestures: for adult animals the outlines of the 'vocabulary' have been described elsewhere (Hinde and Rowell, 1962; Rowell and Hinde, 1962) and they form a system which can convey fairly precise information to other members of the species. Very young monkeys have a limited 'vocabulary'. They make a noise when dislodged from the teat, to which the mother responds by shifting and hugging, a short call which will induce the mother or an aunt to go and pick them up, and a long plaintive call through rounded lips which is made when they have lost all contact with the mother. The face, in spite of its mobile appearance, is curiously expressionless, remaining fixed in what in an adult would indicate confident concentration on a problem.

[1] This work is being carried out in collaboration with R. A. Hinde, and is financed by the Medical Research Council.

35

TABLE I

The two groups of monkeys

	Name	Age	Sex	Breeding status	Introduced	Remarks
Group I	Tom	c. 6 yrs.	M			Father of Eliane
	Lois	?	F	Multipare		Tom's favourite, Eliane's mother
	Eliane		F			Born to Lois 29 Aug. 1960
	Rosie	?	F	Still birth 10 weeks after Eliane born		Well known to Lois
	Priscilla	c. 4 yrs.	F	Nullipare	10 days before Eliane born	
	Bunty	c. 10 yrs.	F	?	21 weeks after Eliane born	
Group II	Boris	c. 10 yrs.	M			Father of Yuri and Vostok
	Ruth	?	F	First baby?		Yuri's mother
	Yuri		M			Born to Ruth 17 April 1961
	Molly	?	F	Multipare		Vostok's mother; paralysed in one hind leg
	Vostok		F			Born to Molly 11 April 1961
	Babs	3–4 yrs.	F	Nullipare	6 weeks before babies born	
	Annie	3–4 yrs.	F	Nullipare	6 weeks before babies born	Boris's favourite

At six weeks they begin to make the long low greeting growl to other animals, who sometimes make pleasure noises in return. Just after this, as the mothers respond less quickly to the call to be picked up, these calls are lengthened and elaborated and a long series is used to 'nag' the mother until, for example, she carries the baby through the swing door.

In the ninth and tenth weeks the babies' ability to communicate suddenly expanded. First they all made the very striking expression 'lip-smacking' which adults use to express something like conciliation. They began to make the pleasure noises and the postures used in initiating grooming, and to groom other animals – especially their mothers – though only briefly. Then the expression indicating fear appeared and with it the geckering screech used by adults to get co-operation from other members of the group when in danger. At about 16 weeks, when the two babies developed mounting behaviour, the submissive posture which is similar to soliciting appeared and was given to all adults occasionally. The threat signals were not developed until later. The first low-intensity threat expressions were seen at five months, the noises and higher-intensity postures did not develop until just over a year.

Starting with noises used in the infant situation, then, the adult communicating patterns are added first to indicate friendliness, then fear, and then, more slowly, aggression.

The blank expression of the first two months can be regarded as having communicative value in its own right. This would be comparable to the juvenile plumage of birds or the first coat of mammals, which lack the provocative patterns of the adult and so, along with their other functions, proclaim that the individuals wearing them are not to be brought into the scheme of adult competition.

Now let us see how the babies actually interacted with other animals, given these available methods of communication.

After birth, all the mothers held their babies to them tightly, hugged them, and rocked them; Lois made pleasure noises to hers. They sat alone more than usual and pushed away other females that came close. They turned their backs on watchers and crouched over the baby. All other females in sight including those in other cages took a keen interest in the babies whenever they looked round, peering at them and making an explosive cough whenever the mother shifted the baby and whenever it turned back to the teat after staring about it (Plate 4). This explosive cough is only heard in the mother-infant-aunt relationship; later one of the aunts makes it almost every time a mother picks up her baby, and only, as far as I know, when the baby's own mother picks it up – which means that relations are recognized between animals known only by sight as well as within the group. The explosive cough is accompanied by head-bobbing and tail-wagging (I think monkeys only wag their tails in this situation).

It is difficult to find a biological function for this very noticeable behaviour, especially since neither mother nor baby seems to take any notice of it.

On Eliane's first day, Priscilla lip-smacked to her. When Lois glared at Priscilla, she gave a fear grin and then looked at the baby and lip-smacked again. It seems that the baby is regarded as another *individual* even at this stage, and not just as a cuddly object, since lip-smacking is characteristically directed at other *monkeys* (including human beings).

On her sixth day, Eliane left her mother and crawled shakily to Rosie, two to three feet away. Rosie turned and presented to her, while Lois watched them both very closely. She came to pick Eliane up after a few seconds, and Rosie fled when she moved. Presenting, for mounting, usually indicates submission, but with a fair degree of confidence in the friendly intentions of the other. Now these gestures of both Rosie and Priscilla were definitely made to the baby, not to its mother (this is easy to see; monkeys look at each other's faces when communicating). On both occasions the baby was accorded the same rank as its mother, who was dominant to both animals. Rank order between newly introduced adults is in theory determined by fighting, though in most cases the animal with territorial rights does all the aggression, and the newcomer doesn't dispute. Here the aunts could be regarded as the territory owners but, although they see the baby as a new individual, there is no attempt to assert their rights. Nor is the baby's close contact with a dominant animal the only reason for respect; females will threaten at another female as she hides behind the male and nobody is confused about where the threat is aimed.

The next day Rosie was again presenting to the baby. Shortly after Lois got up and left it when it came off the nipple. Rosie was still sitting near, watching the baby, and it went to Rosie and clung to her while Rosie made pleasure noises (Plate 5). Lois looked round, came back and groomed it briefly as it clung to Rosie, and then went away again and left them for a few minutes. In the second week, Rosie picked up the baby almost every time Lois left it, and Lois let her hold it for a while and then took it back. But quite often the baby had its back to its aunt as she held it, and it never tried to suckle even when it clung in the proper position. Lois would go the length of the cage away, but always had her eye on her baby, and would rush

38

back to it and take it herself if there was the slightest disturbance. The baby followed its mother with its eyes while clinging to the aunt, and it was quite clear at eight days that this was a temporary substitute, and the baby recognized its mother among two or three others at some distance by sight. This is before it started to follow the mother about, so that 'functional mother' is only tactile, food, and face – not a four-legged back view. It was also behaving differently to the two aunts at this stage, but this might have been reacting to their different degrees of confidence rather than recognizing them as individuals. Sometimes when Rosie was not about, Lois would leave the baby near Priscilla, though she didn't start this until several days after Rosie was allowed to be in charge. Priscilla would crouch over Eliane, watching Lois all the time out of her eye corners. She was nervous of touching the baby and it often climbed out of her arms. Often she watched Eliane intently, occasionally licking her lips which is a sign of nervousness. After a few days she tried to steal the baby – she picked it up and ran. Lois of course gave chase, Priscilla dropped the baby, and Lois retrieved and cuddled it while Rosie chased Priscilla round and round the cage. This happened twice while I was there; but each time Priscilla was allowed to groom Lois within a minute of them settling down.

It is interesting that she dropped the baby, because this never happens when the *mother* grabs the baby and runs. The mother puts her arm across its shoulders, and the baby immediately turns and clings and can hold on without her assistance whatever she does. The whole movement is beautifully co-ordinated and *very* fast. Presumably the baby *would* not cling to an animal that wasn't its mother.

In the third week the baby would try to go to Lois when she came back to Rosie. Rosie didn't always cuddle it, but would sit by it while it tried to climb. By the fourth week there was a continual battle of wills because Lois only left the baby when it was awake, and by now when it was awake it wanted to move and explore, whereas Rosie wanted to cuddle it. Lois kept the balance from a distance; when Rosie was being too restrictive, a glance from Lois at twelve feet was enough to make her let the baby go. Priscilla was only rarely left with the baby, and then Lois watched her the whole time. She daren't restrain the baby, but followed it everywhere (Plate 6), crouched over it, and put her chin on its back.

39

In the fourth week also, Tom made his first gestures towards the baby. He groomed Eliane very gently with his fingertips for a few seconds (this was noticeable because Tom doesn't often groom anybody). Lois watched carefully as she did in the first encounters with the females, and then went away and left them.

Eliane's relations with her two aunts continued without much change until about the eighth week, with Lois usually allowing them access to the baby but occasionally she would turn even on Rosie, without any special provocation, and cuff or threaten her.

Up to the eighth week there is little to say about the aunt relationship for Yuri and Vostok. Whereas Lois was leaving her baby in the first week, and in the second was going some distance away, Ruth did not allow her baby out of arm's reach until he was four weeks old (Plate 7), and Molly effectively kept hers in arm's reach until the seventh week. There was just no opportunity for aunts. The mothers stayed together almost all the time, nursing their babies (Plate 8). Molly made no advances to Yuri, but Ruth was interested in Vostok; she coughed when Molly picked her up, and she would hold one of Vostok's legs as she clung to Molly, or groom her for a few seconds. In all these contacts Vostock was treated by Ruth with exactly the same 'friendly dominance' that she showed to her mother.

The other two females were not allowed near the babies. They hung around the mothers a lot of the time, watching the babies intently and coughing when the mothers handled them. The response of the mothers varied: sometimes they allowed the aunts to huddle and groom, sometimes they glared at them or chased them away. Later when the babies were allowed their first excursions, each mother would pick up her baby at once if Babs made any move towards it. By the fourth week Annie managed to get in a quick groom at both babies while grooming their mothers – changing back to the mother at once if she made the slightest move.

When Yuri was four weeks old, Ruth began to leave him with Molly. Molly still rarely let Vostok explore without holding her tail, so that in the next two weeks both babies were usually with Molly when active. Molly sometimes groomed Yuri or held him by the tail with her free hand, though she let him go if he set off towards his mother. Both mothers were occasionally rough with the other's baby, Ruth much more often; the babies showed no sign of being alarmed by this treatment, and just wandered away rather than

40

running to their own mothers. At four weeks also, Ruth allowed Babs near Yuri and she crouched over him without daring to touch him. The next week Babs presented to him and then invited grooming but Yuri wandered away. (You remember it wasn't till ten weeks the babies were able to make and respond to the signs initiating grooming.)

In the sixth week a new group of behaviour patterns appeared in all the babies, which we call cavorting. It starts with little jumps on the spot and gets more elaborate, including handstands, pouncing and generally throwing the body about. Eliane spent a lot of time doing this whenever she was awake for the next 25 weeks. The other babies rarely do it, and then only for a few seconds at a time; but at the same age they began to play with each other. For the first four weeks they were oddly unaware of each other when playing round their mothers. They grabbed at each other when they bumped but there seemed to be no sense of continuity – each was just another thing to explore each time. This is interesting to compare, I think, with the recognition of *adults* as separate entities which Eliane showed as early as eight days. In the fifth week they began to show some signs of interest in each other, and in the sixth they began to follow and bite and wrestle. The games gradually got more elaborate as locomotor ability improved, in the same way as did Eliane's cavorting. Yuri was nearly always the aggressor, and anyway by four months was noticeably bigger than Vostok. He would start games by throwing himself on her back and biting at her shoulders. In the fifteenth week this sort of play pattern suddenly began to include complete mounting and thrusting patterns, but without erection. Vostok did not respond by standing properly for mounting until about two weeks later, and about two weeks after that she included turning and grooming Yuri's genitals after mounting (which still, at five months, doesn't include erection). Molly frequently intervenes in their wrestling to rescue Vostok, and this can set off a whole chain of interactions. For instance, in the ninth week Yuri bit Vostok, and Molly picked her up and gave a mild threat expression to Yuri. Ruth stalked over and glared at Molly, and then when Ruth turned her back again, Molly caught Yuri and twisted his arm until he pulled away. Later when Yuri became too rough, Vostok would tow him towards Molly till he was near enough for Molly to cuff him.

In the seventh week Ruth and Molly became more tolerant of the other females and allowed them to play with the babies. They rarely cuddled the babies, but touched and pulled at them, crouched over them and sometimes 'mounted' them. They always keep an eye on the mothers who sometimes chase them away. At five months, Babs has a preference for Vostok and sometimes intervenes in their wrestling on her behalf, and Ruth usually ignores this. The growing preference was accompanied by spending more time sitting with Molly and grooming her, and Molly in turn became more friendly to Babs.

From about six weeks all the babies, but Eliane more than the others, began to make advances towards their aunts in connection with foraging behaviour. At six weeks they would try to take food from their mother's hand. Then they began to take a keen interest in feeding and foraging behaviour of all the adults. When one came back from feeding, a baby would go to her and sniff or lick her mouth, apparently to find out what she had eaten. They would go to an adult who was carrying food and try to share the handful. Sometimes they were threatened or pushed away, but on the whole they were tolerated far more than another adult would be in the same circumstances. On the other hand it was only the mothers whose food-gathering behaviour their babies appeared to imitate; the baby would follow its mother closely, watching her movements intently and then doing the same thing itself.

Eliane's cavorting became more and more playing *at* others instead of around them, as if inviting play. All the group became irritated by this and from eight weeks frequently cuffed or jerked at her (the aunts when Lois' back was turned); but this irritation only lasted as long as she was being a nuisance. By nine months her play consisted almost entirely of tormenting the females, playing tag and run; when alone she was fairly sedate, wandering about foraging and exploring. Priscilla was the only one who would occasionally play actively with her. She never tried to torment Tom, of course, but from 12 weeks she would sit with him and share his food, and he would groom her, put his arm round her, and occasionally hold her hips as if for mating. He also wrestled with her, and still does now she is a year old, very gently, and she puts her head and arms between his great fangs.

Boris on the other hand has almost ignored his offspring up to now. I haven't seen any interaction with Vostok at all. In the third week he avoided Yuri, shifting away when he approached. By the fifth week Yuri was a bit afraid of him, and ran to his mother whenever Boris looked at him. I don't know why this happened; Ruth kept him away from Boris, but he showed no sign of fear of his aunts from whom he was also protected. In the sixth week Yuri reached out from Ruth to touch Boris as he went past, and Boris came back and cuffed him, and Yuri squeaked. At four-and-a-half months he still avoided Boris, and even left his mother when she groomed Boris; but at five months he sometimes went and sat near his father. Either way Boris behaved as if he did not exist.

This difference in the amount of interaction with the father is paralleled by the mother's behaviour – Molly avoided Boris all the time, and her baby had never 'met' Boris. Ruth paid little attention to him for the first four months, but then began to groom him fairly often; Lois maintained her position as favourite wife throughout pregnancy and lactation. There may be a further correlation here between the mother's behaviour and menstruation – Lois menstruated straight on after birth, Ruth started at about four months, Molly I don't think had started at five months. But one shouldn't think in terms of cause and effect too soon, because the post-parturition behaviour in each case was a continuation of the patterns shown during pregnancy.

When Eliane was 32 weeks old, Lois died. Rosie took over as mother, carrying Eliane on her belly, and Eliane always ran to her if there was a disturbance. The change occurred as soon as Lois was taken out of the group. After two weeks Eliane had accepted the new situation completely, and you couldn't tell from behaviour that Rosie was not the true mother except that Eliane never tried to suckle although she had still been nursed by Lois. There were some other changes in the group structure – Bunty became much more confident, although Lois had rarely joined in Priscilla's and Rosie's attacks on her. She began to nurse Eliane occasionally as well. Eliane was still effectively the baby of the dominant female but if one uses order of taking food as a rough measure of dominance, whereas Lois was dominant over her baby, as one would expect, Rosie does not take precedence over Eliane. Eliane also seemed to have taken over her mother's position as favourite 'wife'. Tom frequently mounted her during a few weeks up to the age of 11 months, although she was so small. She sat with him often, and he chased

43

any other female who showed any aggression towards her. Thus in this case the status which was accorded to the baby at birth by virtue of her mother had become hers in her own right when the mother's protection was lost at eight months.

Instead of a summary I should like to mention some of the points which I think are most interesting, and the ones which I hope will be answered by further observation.

In the beginning, the aunts did not need to learn, but accepted the babies' status at once – but they may have learned from previous encounters with mothers and babies. Eliane's father also played an important part in establishing her position, especially after Lois' death. Is it because he is young to be alpha in a group, or through some quirk in his upbringing, that he is so tolerant of babies compared with Boris; is it to any baby, to female babies, or to babies of favourites that this extends? How permanent is Eliane's position – will it stand when Rosie has her own baby, for example?

This problem of the origin of social status is important. It is well-known, and this is a good example, that it does not depend only on strength. For the adult monkey social status has an immense influence, not only on physical well-being, from getting the best food and positions, but on the 'intelligence' shown when coping with the environment. It is much easier to concentrate when you can ignore other monkeys, and in our groups it is the dominant animals that learn to undo things. If the young can acquire 'dominance attitudes' by, say, six months, we may be able to account for a bit more of the variability in behaviour of young imported monkeys used in much behaviour work. If a female can really pass on the advantage of dominance to her offspring, it becomes still more important as a biological advantage. The great difference between the mothers' handling of the babies also raises problems, partly unanswerable because we don't know anything of their histories – we must wait till our own reared babies breed. Was Molly's extraordinary protectiveness at first due to her paralysis as I have assumed, or is it within the normal range of behaviour in our conditions? And if because of the paralysis, did it stop when the baby's own locomotion became efficient enough to compensate, or is there anyway a 'step' in the mother's behaviour at about eight weeks? And how does the amount of protection affect the babies' later behaviour – perhaps not how one might predict, because Vostok attempted before the other two the

44

33333333333

dangerous feat of taking titbits from me for instance (eighteen weeks; Eliane not till twenty-six) in spite of her mother's attempts to 'rescue' her. The mother's, and hence the babies', behaviour is apparently greatly influenced by the available companions. Lois had a friend she could trust with the baby and also control. So had Ruth, but Molly was occupied with her own baby and couldn't be used as a baby sitter till later. From Molly's point of view, Ruth, being dominant, couldn't be controlled, and therefore couldn't be trusted, and anyway she was also occupied. And Babs and Annie they had only known a few weeks.

The females' relations with the males also affected the mother's relations with the aunts. The males will mostly support their favourite in a fight, so of the mothers Lois could risk starting an attack where Ruth or Molly dared not. Therefore Lois felt more secure and able to trust other females, even when there was no actual fighting going on.

Then why did the behaviour of the aunts vary so? Here again we can't separate all the possible factors as yet. Priscilla, Babs and Annie all showed more play and intention mounting than strictly 'maternal' patterns. They are all nullipares; on the other hand they were strangers to the mothers at the time of birth, and very fearful of them; so it may be that it needs confidence to be motherly – or it might be that, although fascinated by babies, they don't know how to handle them until they have learned on a co-operative baby of their own.

Discussion following Dr Rowell's paper

ROBERTSON *Could you tell us something about your methods of observing the monkeys? Are you visible to them?*

ROWELL *Yes, they can certainly see us. They take an interest at first, but when they see that we are not going to catch or feed them, they quickly lose interest, except that they resent being looked at in the eyes. I'm sure they would behave slightly differently if we were not there, but I don't think the baby is really affected. We observe them for a minimum of six hours a week, in watches of not less than an hour, usually two hours. During this time we make notes on their general behaviour, but we also use half-minute time sheets for recording in detail the position of the baby with respect to the mother and other monkeys.*

HARLOW *At what age do the babies detach from their mothers?*

ROWELL *In the case of Eliane, when she was six days old. Lois, the mother, encouraged the baby to leave her. As soon as Eliane came off the teat, Lois turned so that her arm came between the teat and the baby and then moved back a bit, and the baby turned and went off to Rosie.*

AINSWORTH *At this age, would she watch her mother much?*

ROWELL *Oh yes, at eight days, for instance, Rosie was holding the baby, but the baby's eyes were following the mother continually, and ignoring the other monkeys in the cage.*

BOWLBY *So that at eight days she can already discriminate her mother. Has she had much opportunity at that age to observe her mother?*

ROWELL *She has had a lot of opportunity to observe her mother's face. The mother frequently bends down, pulls back the baby's face to look at it, and when the baby is awake it looks back at the mother's face.*

BOWLBY *What happens when the baby is sucking?*

ROWELL *It usually has its eyes shut at this age.*

BOWLBY *It's interesting to compare this with Donald Gough's (1962) observation on human babies that even during the first day or two of life, when their eyes are open, they stop scanning when they are sucking and fixate instead; and if they are at the breast, they usually fixate the mother's face.*

DAVID *It seems to me very difficult to tell where the baby is looking. I find that my observation does not always agree with that of the nurse feeding the baby.*

WOLFF *A colleague, Dr Clementina Kuhlman, has recently started watching such behaviour systematically, and I find this same difficulty. Also there are big differences between babies. It depends on how they are held, whether they are bottle-fed or not. My own observations suggest that while they are taking the first ounce or so of milk babies tend to fixate whatever they happen to be looking at, whether it's mother or not; after that they are more easily distracted, but only temporarily if they are still sucking.*

AINSWORTH *I was interested in Thelma Rowell's observation of the infant following its mother with its eyes, because I found just the same in African babies – if they were being held by someone else, they would follow their mother with their eyes, even in a roomful of people.*

BOWLBY *At what age would that be?*

Thelma E. Rowell – Discussion

AINSWORTH *The youngest child in which I noted this response was 18 weeks old. I did not, however, systematically observe following with the eyes, and I suspect that a differential following of the mother with the eyes may well occur at an even younger age.*

ROWELL *When the Rhesus infant is older, it will look all over the place while sucking, or at least while the teat is in the mouth, and this is possible because the teat will stretch a great deal. At this stage the infant could lean back to look at its mother's face, but it is more likely to handle the mother's fur.*

GEWIRTZ *This along with Harry Harlow's work suggests that visual stimuli may be less important for monkeys than, say, the tactile stimuli provided by the mother's fur; the Rhesus infant's early learnings might be based more on stimuli provided through touch and contact than on distal stimuli.*

ROWELL *But you still have to explain how visual recognition occurs at eight days of age. And anyhow, monkeys are very interested in faces. They look at their babies' faces a lot when they are not suckling, and at other monkeys' faces.*

HARLOW *I haven't got such detailed observations, but I agree there is a lot of looking backwards and forwards between mother and baby monkeys from a very early age.*

ROWELL *It varies between mothers. It was characteristic of Lois that she looked at Eliane's face a lot, even getting down so as to be able to look at her face at eye level.*

GEWIRTZ *I was wondering if there might not be some movement or gesture or something the Rhesus infant might do that could provide reinforcing stimuli for the mother when she looks at him?*

ROWELL *I don't think so. Lois would look at Eliane continually, and hop up and down and make pleasure noises. She was obviously thrilled to bits with it.*

BOWLBY *How about the father's attitude?*

ROWELL *He was ill and out of the cage when Eliane was born. I put him back when she was three days old, but it was a long time before he noticed the baby because it was hanging on its mother's belly, and the mother was presenting and he was mounting her. When eventually he saw the baby he looked slightly surprised, half put out his hand to touch it but changed his mind and went away. He took absolutely no more interest for about four weeks, as far as it's possible to ignore an infant monkey playing around. Then after*

47

four weeks the father made a first tentative approach at grooming Eliane.

BOWLBY *At what age does the infant itself start grooming?*

ROWELL *Not until the tenth or eleventh week, though some of the gestures occur before then.*

HARLOW *How did the other father, Boris, behave to his offspring?*

ROWELL *Well, they are five months old now, and he has almost entirely avoided them always – deliberately avoided them if necessary.[1] Whereas Tom now regards Eliane, who is still pre-adolescent, as his favourite. He sits with her, plays with her and defends her from the others.*

MICHELL *Have you any idea why Rosie became Eliane's favourite aunt? Was it because she was pregnant, and possibly lactating?*

ROWELL *She did not lactate, and Eliane did not try to suckle from her. Her pregnancy may have had an effect, but I think it is more likely that she was the only suitable one to be a favourite aunt, because she had been very friendly with Lois, the mother. In the other group only Molly was friendly with Ruth, and she was busy with her own baby.*

SCHAFFER *When Lois the mother died it seems extraordinary that Eliane was not more upset.*

ROWELL *Well this is not like a usual case of separation because the infant's environment remained exactly the same, except that the mother went. Also Lois died gradually and wasn't very effective in the last few days. There was a lot of nagging calling going on because the baby was never satisfied by the mother. Also Eliane had an excellent substitute mother in Rosie.*

BOWLBY *The circumstances were about as favourable as they could be for the infant. In comparable cases with human babies of about two years, upsets lasting only a week or so are common.*

ROWELL *And Eliane at 33 weeks was more equivalent to a six-year-old child.*

GUNTHER *Are the mothers expert with their babies?*

ROWELL *It depends partly on whether it is the first baby or not. Ruth was primiparous. She held her baby upside down for a long time,*

[1] Boris began to 'mate' with Vostok at 11 months, and began to play and wrestle with Yuri at 13 months. He is much more tolerant of his new offspring of this year, and allows them to climb on him (T. R. 1962).

and when it was the right way up she held it so high that the baby could not find the nipples.[1]

AMBROSE *There are obviously broad limits with regard to what the mother considers to be the consummatory position.*

ROWELL *Yes, then the baby wriggles about until it reaches what it considers is its consummatory position.*

HINDE *Ruth also left the placenta dangling and the cord got caught on a branch. I tried to release it, and immediately Ruth fled and the baby was jerked off her, and swung by the cord beneath the perch. The mother then returned and grabbed her infant in a quite unconventional way. What happened indicated that the important thing to the mother was to cuddle her baby, and not the use of any specific motor pattern. The method of holding the baby was very variable.*

AMBROSE *Could you say at what age you first saw conflict behaviour, attempting to do two things at once?*

ROWELL *There is rapid alternation of going to the mother, holding the nipple for a second, away again, and alternating; but here they are doing two things successively. The first approach-avoidance conflict I can remember is when they start taking food from me. They make a fright expression as they come closer (nine months).*

AINSWORTH *At what age do you see a clear-cut fright response?*

ROWELL *At 10 weeks; but much earlier, at a week old, babies make a long drawn out call if the mother goes away entirely.*

HARLOW *If the babies become frightened when they are separated from their mothers, do they go straight to them?*

ROWELL *Yes, but they usually don't get the chance because the mother goes to the infant so quickly.*

HARLOW *Do the aunts go as well?*

ROWELL *If the baby makes a fright noise, all the aunts make intention movements, but the mother is by the baby before they have time to move.*

---

[1] Since then we have had some very efficient primipares (T. R.).

PART II

Human Studies

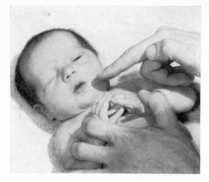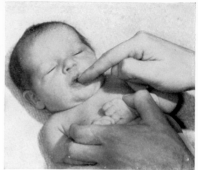

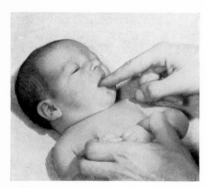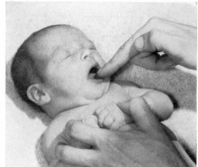

PLATE 9 *a-d*. The rooting response. To a tactile stimulus in the perioral area, the newborn baby turns his head towards the stimulated side (*a, b, above*) opens the mouth (*c, below left*) and grasps with the lips (*d, below right*)

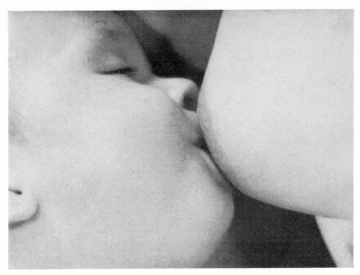

PLATE 10. Sucking on the breast
(From the film *Die Entwicklung der kindlichen Motorik*,
Prechtl, Göttingen, 1953)

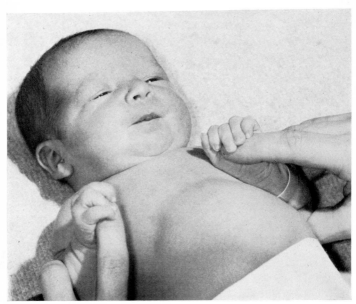

PLATE 11. Grasping with the hands. To a tactile stimulation of the palms,
the fingers are flexed and grasp an object

The Mother-Child Interaction in Babies
with Minimal Brain Damage (a Follow-up Study)[1]

H. F. R. PRECHTL

Newborn babies show a series of behaviour patterns which are essential for establishing a normal child-mother interaction: rooting (Plate 9a, b, c, d), sucking (Plate 10), grasping (Plate 11), the regular changes of the organism's state between sleep, wakefulness and activity and crying (Plate 12a, b, c) and later on smiling (Plate 13a, b). It seems important for every mother, that her baby should show the usual amount of motility and activity, that he has a normal tonus and that the mother is able to pacify him when he is upset.

There is no doubt that a baby with severe brain damage may cause psychological difficulties in a mother. However, there is a broad range of minor abnormalities of the central nervous system, the so-called 'syndrome of minimal brain damage', mostly sequelae of pre- or para-natal complication, which, although they change most of the infant's behaviour patterns distinctly, are not alarming enough for the mother to consult a physician right away. Nevertheless such a child can irritate his mother considerably and give her an over-anxious, overprotective or rejecting attitude towards her child.

We have tried experimentally to check such a hypothesis, which is based on daily clinical experience.

Some years ago I became interested in the neurological examination of the newborn baby and young infant. We have studied, during the first nine days of life, more than 1000 newborns with a history of pre- and/or para-natal complications. Our neurological examination includes a careful observation of spontaneous posture, activity and motility, the changes of states, and a large number of responses. It

---

[1] This study was supported in part by a grant from the Association for the Aid of Crippled Children, New York.

E   53

also takes into account information about the general behaviour and the feeding of the infant.

From a set of distinct syndromes of minimal brain damage in the newborn baby I would like to mention here only two:

1. The hypokinetic child, who is very often hypotonic, drowsy and apathetic, sucks slowly and poorly, and responds only very weakly to various stimulations. Because the baby cries less than normal infants, the mother considers him to be a 'sweet baby'. On the other hand, since the baby is hypotonic, the mother is sometimes frightened that she may harm the floppy baby in the bath or while she is swaddling him.

2. Quite another clinical picture is given by the syndrome we have called the 'hyperexcitability syndrome'. The babies belonging to this category are hyperkinetic, often hypertonic, cry more than normal babies, show sudden changes of state from being drowsy and difficult to arouse, to being wide awake, crying and difficult to pacify. Most of them are vigorous suckers. Nearly all of their responses are exaggerated and have a remarkably low threshold; in particular the Moro response is very striking (Plate 14*a*, *b*). These hyperexcitable children have as a most striking symptom a tremor of low frequency (about 3–4/sec) and high amplitude. Because of the low threshold of the Moro response these babies react to the approach of every person with a Moro response. This often gives mothers the impression of having frightened their baby and, in fact, mothers of such children have told me repeatedly that their baby is very easily startled.

Although in all the cases we have studied, the mothers did not realize that these symptoms were a sign of brain dysfunction, these types of response and behaviour patterns were a source of distress, worry and grief to the mothers.

In a pilot longitudinal follow-up study of a small group of hyper-excitable children and a matched control group, Mrs van der Gaag (M.D.) from our team examined the children in their homes every three months during their first year and made observations of the maternal attitudes. Although this study is still in progress and the results are preliminary, I would like to mention a few observations. All the children were the firstborns, all families came from similar socio-economic classes (lower middle class), and all of them live in Groningen. The ages of the mothers and the birth weights of the children were similar.

First of all we were struck by the fact that the symptoms of hyperexcitability mentioned above persisted for several months and in one case up to nine months (Table 2) and that a large difference

TABLE 2

Neurological findings in the abnormal group

♂/Birth-♀ weight	Pre- and paranatal complication	Neo-natal	8–14 weeks	20–27 weeks	40–46 weeks	Maternal attitude
♂ 3010	Foetal distress	He, L	He, L	He, L	He, L	positive
♂ 4250	Toxaemia and foetal distress Caesarean section	He, L	He, L	L	?	rejecting
♂ 4080	Foetal distress	He, L	He, L	He, L	L	rejecting
♂ 3190	Toxaemia	He	no	no	no	rejecting
♀ 2520	Toxaemia Forcipal extraction	He, L	He, L	He, L	L	over-anxious
♀ 2500	Toxaemia Foetal distress	He	He	He	no	over-anxious
♀ 2300	Foetal distress Forcipal extraction	He, L	L	L	no	over-anxious
♀ 3200	Toxaemia Foetal distress Forcipal extraction	He, L	L	L	L	rejecting

Symbols: He = Hyperexcitability syndrome; L = asymmetry of tonus and/or responses.

in the developmental quotients (Table 3) in the two groups was found in the beginning, but disappeared later. For a mother these symptoms are therefore not simply a phenomenon lasting only for the first days of her baby's life, but represent to her signs of the baby's 'temperament' and 'character'. It is at least plausible that these hyper-excitability symptoms may have an influence on the pattern of mothering. I might remark here that my own experience as well as those of my co-workers during the neurological examination was,

TABLE 3

Developmental quotients (Griffiths)
(the D.Q. are given in averages)

Age in weeks when tested	NORMAL GROUP (10 infants)				
	Locomotor	Personal-social	Hearing/speech	Eye and hand	Perform-ance
8–14	151	175	141	115	86
20–27	110	129	125	121	121
40–46	104	100	100	93	92
ABNORMAL GROUP (8 infants)					
8–14	136	152	120	82	85
20–27	100	125	113	118	123
40–46	96	96	97	91	99

that we were 'annoyed' by these infants, because of their exaggerated reactions and their sudden changes in state; sometimes they cried vigorously and it was impossible to pacify them either by rocking or letting them suck the examiner's finger, the next moment the baby was drowsy and did not react at all.

The findings of the longitudinal follow-up study have been, that in the case of seven out of eight abnormal babies the examiner noticed that the mothers did not show a harmonious, positive attitude to their baby after a few months. All of the problems which a mother usually meets with in her first child, were more pronounced and the mothers were anxious whether they treated the baby correctly. In the first place they did not think that the source of the trouble was in the baby itself, but rather that they were 'mishandling' their child. In the second place the baby's behaviour failed to satisfy the mother's expectations, and as a result the mother became disquieted. However, in the control groups of 10 normal babies, who were followed up in the same way, only one mother was troubled and overanxious, in the other cases the child-mother relation seems harmonious.

The diagnoses of the mothers' attitudes, as given in Table 2, were based on direct observations and interviews with the mothers. They have not yet been objectified by psychological tests, but we have started testing both groups with the 'Parental Attitude Research Instrument' as described by Schaefer and Bell (1958).

The results of the PARI applied to seven mothers of the control group have been compared with those of seven mothers with abnormal babies. Although the groups have been very small, significant differences could be found. In the pathological group the mothers showed a higher 'approval of activity' of the child ($p = 0.02$), a greater 'fostering dependency' ($p = 0.05$) and less rejection of the 'home making role' ($p = 0.05$). These findings give evidence of the fact that the mothers of abnormal babies, although they are not aware of it consciously, are more protective and dominant.

These results are supported by another of our studies. Out of 1000 newborn babies, born after one or other pre- or para-natal complication, the oldest 128 were asked to return for a follow-up examination. Of these, 116 children appeared and three had died in the meantime. The age at the time of the follow-up examination was between $1\frac{1}{2}$ years and 4 years and 2 months. The examiner (Dr J. Dijkstra) did not know the neonatal findings. Out of 54 neonatally abnormal babies, 68 per cent were found to be neurologically abnormal later on; out of 53 neonatally normal babies only 8 per cent were found to be abnormal later on. Out of 32 children who suffered from the hyperexcitability syndrome in the newborn period, 70 per cent showed the choreiform syndrome later on (Prechtl 1961).

The choreiform syndrome (Prechtl and Stemmer, 1959, 1962) is characterized by frequent small chorea-like twitches in all muscles including the eye-muscles, hyperactivity, typical behaviour problems such as short concentration span, fluctuation of attention and instability of mood. These children have learning difficulties when they are at school (Prechtl, 1962).

In addition to the neurological abnormalities noted in children who had also signs of abnormality in the neonatal period, 65 per cent showed one or more behaviour problems, while of those children who had been found normal at the neonatal examination, only 22 per cent had behaviour problems.

Although in this study we have not yet been especially dealing with maternal behaviour, we did record some aspects of the maternal attitude in the protocols. In the neonatally normal group (53 cases), the mothers were in seven cases concerned and worried about their children. In the neonatally abnormal group on the other hand (54 cases), 23 mothers were reported to be concerned and worried.

Based on these data we may ascertain that abnormal behaviour in an infant can influence and change the mothering and maternal attitude. Neurologically abnormal babies do not make adequate partners in the child-mother interaction.

A weak point, however, is that we do not know anything about the personality of the mothers before they had their babies, and what the influence of a difficult delivery itself may be, as shown by Davids *et al.* (1961). We have now started a study to fill this gap and to carry out a longitudinal follow-up study of the maternal attitude, beginning with an examination of the 'pre-maternal' personality. In this way we hope to find out more about the influence of a neurotic mother on her baby and about the effect of an abnormal baby on a healthy mother.

This is also important in another respect. It has been shown by Cramond (1954) and Scott and Thomson (1956), that psychological factors can give rise to uterine dysfunction during labour. Since psychological factors can cause a prolonged labour, they may also be seen as the aetiological factors of brain lesions in the baby. The personalities of the mothers with uterine dysfunction were found to be characterized 'by suppression or repression of feelings of tension. The patients who exhibited this temperament tended to be reserved, even suspicious, and had difficulty in talking about themselves and their problems. It was noted that they were more conventional than normal' (Cramond, 1954).

Although most of our cases had antenatal or para-natal complications such as toxaemia, asphyxia and so on, there is a group of cases with prolonged labour in which a foetal distress with brady-cardia and post partum apnea occurred. We may assume that psychological factors play a part in this complication. In addition we should not forget that psychological stresses during pregnancy may act as aetiological factors of brain lesion in the foetus. Table 4 attempts to summarize the relationships.

This pattern of factors sheds some light on those discussions in child psychiatry, which try to solve the question whether a behaviour problem should be explained as organic or psychogenic. My attempt

TABLE 4

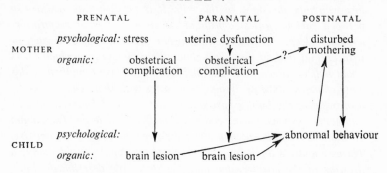

was to show the intimate interaction of both of these factors and we hope that in this way we may come to a better understanding and treatment of the psychopathology of children. We are still at a stage of hypothesis and a lot of experimental work will be necessary to check the foregoing statements.

Acknowledgements

My thanks are due to Miss H. C. Weststrate, Ph.D., and M. J. D. Henriquez y Pimentel, Ph.D., for their analyses of the PARIs.

Discussion following Dr Prechtl's paper

SCHAFFER *I wonder if you could tell me something about the reliability of the neurological examination. Would two people using your method get more or less the same diagnosis?*

PRECHTL *We have carried out a reliability study between scorers. Three examiners scored simultaneously the responses we look at in the neurological examination, using the quantitative scale we have designed. Agreement was between 80 and 96 per cent for all three examiners, and there were no systematic deviations. This high reliability is the result of a long and intensive training programme as well as strict definitions of the scales.*

AINSWORTH *Could you give us some details of your method?*

PRECHTL *I can give you a rough sketch. We do the examination two hours after the last feeding and an hour before the next. The baby's temperature is taken, since this influences the internal condition.*

Then probably the most crucial stage is a long period of examination just watching the baby in the crib. It is necessary to distinguish between various states – profound sleep with regular respiration, irregular sleep, drowsiness, wide awake activity without crying, or with crying, and so on. Throughout the examination, which takes about half or three-quarters of an hour, we note continually how this state changes, since everything else varies with that. Then we make a drawing of the baby's position; we note its facial movements, its autonomic responses – the colour of the skin and so on. Then about 10 minutes is spent watching the baby's spontaneous motor activity. Then we undress the baby, put him on an examination table, make a drawing of the posture, and note the state. We describe the kind, tempo, symmetry and intensity of the motor activity; we note the tremor, the type and regularity of respiration, the skin, the skull and eye movements, the muscle tone, and muscle power all over the body; the skin, abdominal and muscle reflexes and so on. All the usual neurological items. But always the tests are related to the baby's state, because we have found this to be crucial. For instance, in a drowsy baby with a head drop there is no Moro response, but in a crying baby with a head drop you get a very strong Moro. Another way of producing the Moro response is to push the mattress the baby is lying on, and here there is a high response in irregular sleep, a fairly high incidence in drowsy babies, but none at all in a wide awake crying baby. In other words, the results depend on the method used and on the baby's state. The same principle applies to oral responses, to sucking, rooting, grasping and so on. Another important point about our technique is that, instead of testing the cranial nerves in order from one to twelve, we give the least disturbing tests first, and gradually work up to the more disturbing ones. Also we note the response caused by the test itself. For instance if the baby cries after having the Moro tested, that may be significant.

GUNTHER *I think I should add that this method which Dr Prechtl has invented is very beautiful indeed, and has come to be called the Groningen method.*

BOWLBY *Is the examination as efficient at three or six months?*

PRECHTL *Yes, it is.*

MICHELL *Is there any parallel increase in knowledge regarding the EEG in infancy? Are there any links with your neurological syndromes?*

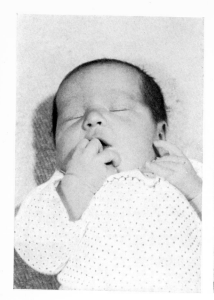
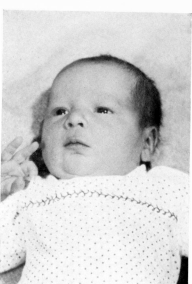
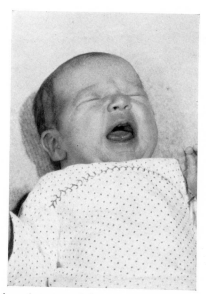

PLATE 12. Behavioural states. *a* (*above left*) irregular sleep with mouthing; *b* (*above right*) awake and alert; *c* (*below*) active and crying.

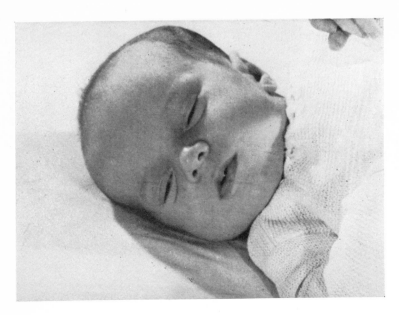

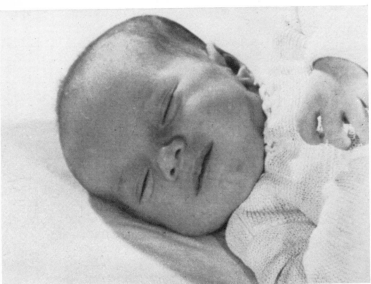

PLATE 13a–b. Smiling response in a 9-day-old newborn. a (*above*) at rest and drowsy; b (*below*) halfsided smiling on the left side of the baby's face (From the same film as Plate 10)

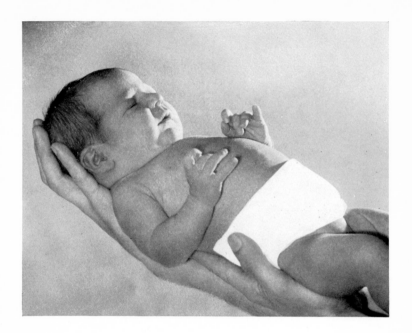

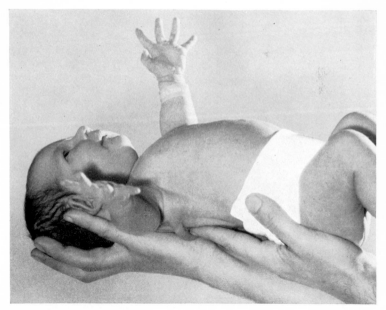

PLATE 14. Moro-response. Dropping the head a few cm, the baby responds with an abduction and extension of the arms.

PLATE 15 *a* (*left*). Paulo at 52 weeks

PLATE 15 *b* (*right*). William (37 weeks) and his mother

PLATE 15 *c* (*left*). Nabatanzi (56 weeks) and her mother

PLATE 15 *d* (*right*). Nakiku at 54 weeks

PRECHTL *The EEG is very useful for finding out if there is any epileptic activity, but I think that otherwise it is not very useful in the first year. I was very interested to hear that Dr Windle has the same experience with monkeys. He has a film of a monkey with severe brain damage, but a completely normal EEG. But it's possible that electro-myography might be more useful. We have tried taking electro-myographs with surface electrodes that don't harm the baby at all. What we found was that the hyper-excitability syndrome produces an EMG pattern very like that from an adult with Parkinson's disease.*

SCHAFFER *I am not clear whether you have independent evidence that the pathological group has brain damage?*

PRECHTL *No, I have no evidence other than from the neurological examination; and the brain damage I have in mind could be biochemical as well as structural. What I am testing is function – we don't look at the nervous system directly.*

FOSS *Is there a sudden transition between the pathological and normal groups or are they on a continuum?*

PRECHTL *There's no sudden transition. It requires an accumulation of symptoms before we decide that a child is pathological. Normal children are hyperkinetic when they are hungry, but they don't have the other symptoms which contribute to our hyperkinesis syndrome.*

BOWLBY *But aren't you influenced at all by the records of the obstetricians in deciding whether or not to examine a baby?*

PRECHTL *We do not know at the moment of the examination if anything was wrong in the history of the baby. Later we get detailed obstetrical information which is the basis of our correlation of obstetrical complications and neurological symptomatology.*

MICHELL *Do you have the impression that the hyperkinetic group can be divided into those with disturbance in brain function and those with disturbed relationships?*

PRECHTL *Hardly, because they are in the first day of life; though it might be possible to make this distinction later on older children.*

BOWLBY *Would you say that the eight cases you have selected to follow up are extreme cases?*

PRECHTL *They are clear-cut rather than extreme.*

BERNSTEIN *In your pathological group, are there any cases of epilepsy or spasticity?*

PRECHTL *No.*

AMBROSE *It would be very useful if one could separate those cases where the abnormality is in different systems, so to speak. For instance, the hyperexcitability seems to be concerned with abnormality of sensory input – very low thresholds perhaps; and other abnormalities such as tremor and lateralization might be more on the motor side; there might also be motivational and learning abnormalities. And all of these do not necessarily go together.*

MICHELL *In some sensitive babies, it is said (Bergman and Escalona, 1949) that there is greater sensitivity in one sensory modality than in the others. Have you found anything like that in the hyperkinetic group?*

PRECHTL *No. I would say that they are more generally sensitive both on the sensory and efferent sides.*

WOLFF *In any of your groups, did you by any chance have any elective caesarean sections?*

PRECHTL *Very few if any, in such a small sample.*

WOLFF *The reason I ask is that I have the impression, from a minute sample, that children from such a delivery are much more alert at first. But it may be because of the anaesthetic difference.*

BERNSTEIN *I would agree with your observation, and I think they are also more hypotonic.*

PRECHTL *In the group I am reporting here, the mothers were given nothing but pure oxygen. But there is certainly a relationship between the use of anaesthetics and hypotonia.*

RHEINGOLD *As you know there is a large study being made in the States of all babies born to mothers at maternity clinics, and it seems that the incidence of baby pathology is much higher when mothers come from lower socio-economic groups. Perhaps this is another factor?*

PRECHTL *But there is also a higher incidence of obstetric complications in such groups. Our obstetrician is able to predict fairly well where a labour will be difficult or not, but I don't know if socio-economic background is one of his cues.*

FOSS *As you yourself have said, the way a mother reacts to a baby which is diagnosed as neurologically abnormal will probably be important in determining the future of the child; and I suppose these reactions might vary between socio-economic groups. It seems to be very difficult to disentangle all the factors at work. You said that*

H. F. R. Prechtl – Discussion

the mother's personality affects the pregnancy, and this may produce a physical result on the baby which in turn results in the mother behaving differently towards the baby. Perhaps the mother's personality and the kind of pregnancy she has may have a common determinant, for instance, hormonal?

PRECHTL *The sort of evidence I had in mind comes from psychological studies (Cramond, 1954; Scott and Thomson, 1956), which show interrelations between type of pregnancy, muscle tensions and so on, and personality and duration of partus which of course has an influence on oxygenation of the foetus, and this in turn influences the brain. I agree that it is necessary to keep an eye on both physical and psychological determinants all the time.*

ROWELL *You haven't mentioned to what extent the babies' abnormalities might be genetically determined. I suppose you can't get any evidence on what sort of births the parents had?*

PRECHTL *The fact that we had 15 per cent abnormalities in newborns in the control group shows that we haven't controlled everything. It's possible that genetic factors are having an effect, and possibly infection also. But I can't give you any figures yet.*

BOWLBY *Perhaps we could turn to your studies of older children. Do symptoms drop out as a child gets older?*

PRECHTL *I would say that they change. For instance, at nine months the tremor may disappear, but is replaced by choreiformic activity. On the other hand, hyper-activity remains.*

AINSWORTH *I was under the impression that minimal brain damage isn't manifest in behaviour until a child is some years older.*

PRECHTL *One must distinguish between behavioural and neurological manifestations. The neurological ones can be seen at any time.*

FOSS *Are you finding that the percentage of neurologically abnormal schoolchildren is about the same as the percentage of abnormal babies?*

PRECHTL *Well, in the population study going on in Arnhem now in elementary schools, 20 per cent of the boys and 9 per cent of the girls have choreic activity, and that's one symptom only.*

BEINTEMA *That compares with 16 per cent in babies where there has been no obstetric complication, and this rises to something like two-thirds for the group with complications.*

BOWLBY *That adds up to an awful lot of defective babies.*

63

PRECHTL *But you must remember that the hospital group are already selected. In Holland many mothers still have their babies at home.*

BOWLBY *If the incidence is so high, and the abnormality correlates with behaviour disorder, then there is quite a problem.*

PRECHTL *I agree. In one study we selected 50 five-year-old kindergarten children with choreiformic activity, and a matched group of 50 normal children. The choreics showed inferior school reports, at a 1 per cent level of significance. So that we have a highly predictive technique. In fact, it's surprising how much you can predict if you look for half a minute at a child who sticks out his hands.*

BOWLBY *If such a large fraction of the child population is involved as you say, it's obvious that paediatricians and teachers should be made aware of the problems.*

FOSS *Would you favour special schools for these children?*

BOWLBY *No, it would be against the modern trend of avoiding segregation. I think the notion of special schools is a thoroughly bad one, except for extreme cases.*

PRECHTL *In Holland there are classes with more than 50 children, and it's quite a problem for a teacher if he has 10 hyperkinetic children who aren't listening. There may have to be special classes at any rate.*

AINSWORTH *I can think of a child with an I.Q. of about 105 who was suspected of having minimal brain damage from psychological tests, and this was confirmed in neurological examination. The other children in the family had I.Q.s of around 130, and the parents were rather compulsive professional people who had high standards for the children. It was obvious in this case that the parents should have relaxed their academic standard for this child. Now this situation must be quite common.*

PRECHTL *There may be exceptions. Most mothers of choreic children will not have noticed much wrong – the child will have been easily startled as a baby, and very active later and a little bit clumsy in movements; but it's only when they get to school that trouble starts – unless they have a high I.Q. With a really high I.Q. they can be as choreic as you like, and still cope.*

THOMAS *But may there not be emotional troubles, tantrums and so on?*

PRECHTL *They may tend to be more aggressive, and more accident prone; and they may be inadequately anxious. For instance a choreic boy might try to fight another boy far bigger than himself, or run into a car, and in neither case will he seem to worry much.*

BOWLBY *From a mental health point of view, this work seems tremendously important. Most public health measures of a preventative kind are based on selecting certain groups at risk and giving them special attention. You seem to have discovered an important group at risk, which can be diagnosed easily.*

MICHELL *Dr Rose (1961) of the Children's Hospital, Philadelphia, has a programme of therapeutic intervention for such groups, and the preliminary papers are most interesting. His children at risk cover a wide range of categories – neonatal difficulties, desertion by father, rhesus babies, and so on – and it seems to me that his kind of programme could be extended to include your group of children.*

GUNTHER *One of the things one would like to know from Heinz Prechtl is what you should tell the mother, and when. If you rush from the labour ward to a mother, and tell her 'You've just had a mongol', that child is absolutely certain to go straight into an institution. But if telling the mother is put off a few weeks, she will have developed affection for the baby, and is more likely to make a job of looking after it. In the case of brain damaged children, what is the situation? And I think the father's attitude matters a lot too; because if he thinks he has a dud baby, this reacts on the mother.*

MICHELL *The question of intervention is very difficult. Dr Rose has found that some paediatricians succeed in making the situation worse through intervention.*

PRECHTL *We need more information. It is my impression that mothers of babies with gross brain damage who are obviously abnormal, often adjust to the situation better than mothers of babies with minimal damage, who do not know that the baby is abnormal, and seem to repress their difficulties.*

AINSWORTH *Some parents seem to be comforted to find that there is a valid basis for the child's difficulties, and that the trouble is not all their own fault. I should think that with a school-age child it might be very important for the parents to know, so that they can stop putting pressure on the child.*

PRECHTL *Yes. That's exactly the point. These children sometimes give a perfect performance one moment and fail miserably the next. They have this waxing and waning of concentration, so that what they need are bouts of 10-minute lessons, then breaks; and they certainly can't sit still for 45 minutes. What they usually get is one extra lesson when the other children have finished! Also they are often backwards at reading and writing: they are unable to perform fine motor co-ordinations because of minute muscle twitches. They really need special teaching, and the parents should certainly be told why they appear to be bad at learning.*

MICHELL *I think one shouldn't underestimate the amount of work involved in therapeutic intervention. Just a single explanation to the family won't often achieve much.*

The Development of Infant-Mother Interaction among the Ganda[1]

MARY D. AINSWORTH

The study that I am going to report to you today is a short-term longitudinal study of a small sample of East African infants and their
mothers. The study occupied nine months of a period in 1954–5
while I was in Uganda. I was concerned with describing the methods
of infant care used by present-day Ganda and with ascertaining their
influence on the development of the child, and particularly on the
development of his relationship with his mother.

When planning this study my focus of interest was on the ancient
practice, still said to be followed in many Ganda families, of separating the child from his mother at the time of weaning and sending him
away to be reared by relatives. As it happened, only one child in my
sample was separated, and therefore I mention this initial interest
only because the plan of the study was determined by it. My expert
informants told me that one-third to one-half of Ganda infants were
separated, and that the separation occurred at weaning, and that
weaning now took place at about 12 months of age. Since I had
only nine months available for the study, I planned to select a sample

[1] This study was supported by the East African Institute of Social
Research, Makerere College, Kampala, Uganda, and, during the phase of
data analysis, by United States Public Health Service Grant M4644.
Gratitude is expressed to these institutions for their support, and to the
following for their invaluable co-operation: to Dr Audrey I. Richards,
then Director of the EAISR, for her permissive help and advice throughout; to Mrs Katie Kibuka, as a sensitive field-worker, a loyal assistant and
a good interpreter; to Dr Hebe Welbourn, of the Uganda Medical Service,
for her interest in Ganda babies and for the medical service which was the
backbone of our programme of help to the subjects in return for their
co-operation; and to all the many Ganda who were helpful, but especially
to the mothers and other caretakers of the Ganda infants who became good
friends as well as valued informants.

67

of unweaned infants in the last half of the first year of life (or older), to observe the nature of the attachment they had already established with their mothers, to follow them through weaning, to observe their reactions to it, and to separation in those cases in which that also occurred.

As it became increasingly apparent that my informants had been mistaken in some of their facts about separation, and that my 'natural experiment' was not going to work out, I turned my attention increasingly towards the development of infant-mother attachment, and away from the effects of its disruption; to implement this new plan I included younger infants in my sample so that the age range was from birth to 24 months, with major emphasis on the period between 2 and 14 months.

I should say a few words about *preliminary procedures* intended to elicit and maintain the co-operation of a sample of mothers – a task difficult enough under ordinary circumstances, and this was a time when political crisis made the Ganda reluctant to co-operate with Europeans. In preparing for the research, I learned the local language, Luganda, well enough to exchange the elaborate customary greetings, and to maintain simple communication without help. For interviewing, I required the services of an interpreter. To gain access to a sample of infants, a time-consuming and difficult series of steps were necessary; I worked through a hierarchy of chiefs, and explained my purposes first to them, then to the people of the villages in public meetings, and finally to individual families who were considering volunteering.

In explaining the purpose of the research I reminded the people that the customs of the Ganda with respect to infant care differed from those of Europeans. I said that I was sure that some of their customs were better for the babies than those of Europeans, although I was equally sure that some of the European customs were better. I emphasized, however, that the only way to find out which were the better customs was to study both sets, and I proposed to study the way that *they* did things. This seemed to make sense to my informants, but it also limited my sphere of legitimate inquiry to the infant himself and to questions obviously related to child care.

I wished to avoid being drawn into giving advice in regard to infant care, but felt bound to give the mothers ample return for their co-operation. Since their chief motivation for co-operating was that it

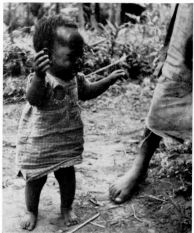

PLATE 16 *a* (*left*). Muhamidi (34 weeks) and his mother

PLATE 16 *b* (*right*). Sulaimani (35 weeks) near his mother

PLATE 16 *c* (*left*). Waswa and Nakato (26 weeks) with their mother

PLATE 16 *d* (*right*). Nora (39 weeks)

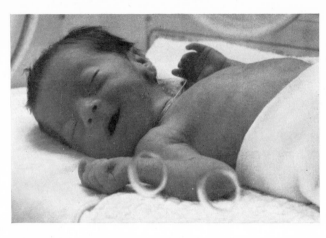

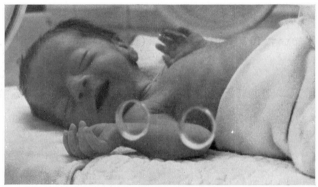

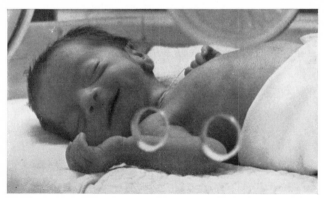

PLATE 17. 30-week gestation – normal premature 'asleep'

might be helpful to the child, the focus of help was on medical services, and in this I was given full support by the director of a travelling clinic, which provided diagnosis and treatment in the case of illness as well as serving as a well-baby clinic. I provided transportation to this clinic, which came every fortnight to the district where my subjects lived; I also gave emergency transportation to hospital when this was required. I dispensed dried skim milk to those who wanted it, and medicines as required to follow through the clinic's treatments. We found it impossible to withhold advice and help about nutrition; fortunately, my interpreter was well-informed about ways of adapting locally available foods to make an adequate supplementary diet for infants.

These services were much appreciated; because of them and because of the friendships that inevitably grew up through repeated contacts, we were able to establish excellent co-operation and to obtain what I believe to be reliable information.

The first mothers who agreed to work with us could be described only as suspicious and reluctant volunteers; but, as time went on, not only did they become friends, but their friends and neighbours became eager to gain the advantages of participating in the research. More volunteers offered themselves and their infants than could be included. The sample is, however, not a random sample in any way, and, moreover, there is no way to obtain a random sample in this kind of setting.

The Ganda and how they live

Now I should make a few remarks about the Ganda and how they live. The subjects of my research lived in six villages about fifteen miles from Kampala. These villages consist of scattered homesteads; one village melts into another without any clear boundary. Each house has an acre or so of land around it, usually consisting of a garden; sometimes the garden is at some distance from the house because better soil is to be found there. It is the role of the woman to cultivate the garden to provide food for the family. The staple is plantain, but it is supplemented by a variety of vegetables and other fruits. The woman spends every morning digging in the garden; how much time she spends depends upon whether the garden is new or well-established, and upon how many mouths she has to feed.

The role of the husband in present-day Uganda is to provide cash for clothing and other necessities – such as school fees for the children, animal foods such as meat, milk and butter, and transportation for himself by bicycle, motor-cycle or even motor-car. Some of the men earn money by raising cash crops such as cotton or coffee; others are employed, either commuting daily to their work, or with jobs so far away that they can get home only on weekends, or perhaps only three or four times a year. In Table 5 the fathers' occupations are shown for this sample, and the extent to which each was able to be home.

The houses are now rectangular and divided into several rooms, most are made of mud and wattle and have thatched roofs and earthen floors; some of the larger and more elaborate of these are attractive and comfortable. The more affluent live in houses of cement block, with red tile roofs and cement floors. Most of the houses have a few pieces of European furniture; the husbands, who are more acculturated, like to sit on chairs, but the women and children nearly all sit on mats on the floor.

In the afternoons the Ganda housewife characteristically goes to visit friends, taking along her babies and young children, or she receives visits. It was during this visiting period that our interviews took place, and our sessions had much the quality of a visit. Most Ganda babies, when they are awake, are held by somebody, propped up in the lap and viewing the assembled group. Later, when they can sit unsupported, they may be placed on the floor, but still in the circle of sociability. When they begin to crawl they are able through their own efforts to reach anybody or anything in the room. Thus, the afternoon visiting hour gave us an excellent opportunity to observe infant-mother interaction under circumstances in which the child was largely free to initiate or terminate an interaction on his own account, and where the mother, although attending to the child, also had demands placed upon her by others, and one could observe how she handled the conflicting demands.

Ganda women clothe themselves in a modest but graceful garment with a square neck, short sleeves, and a skirt sweeping to the floor. Although their babies are in frequent contact with them, and may well be carried in a sling on their backs if they are to be carried for any distance, they are not in direct contact with their mothers' skins, except possibly at night in the case of the small proportion of

70

TABLE 5

Background facts about the sample

	Name	Sex	Age at beginning (mos.)	Age at end (mos.)	Religion	Parents' marital situation	Father at home	Father's occupation	Number of siblings (full, living)
SECURE-ATTACHED	1. Paulo	M	6½	13½	RC	Monogam.	Occ.	Surveyor	2
	2. Sembajwe	M	19½	24	C of E	Monogam.	Weekends	Merchant	0
	3. Juko	M	4½	8	Moslem	Monogam.	Evenings	Health Dept. ?	0
	4. Senvuma	M	8	17½	RC	Mother not married	None	?	4
	5. Petero	M	2	8½	RC	Monogam.	Weekends	Surveyor	1
	6. Mutebe	M	9	12	RC	Separated	Occ.	?	0
	7. Nakiku	F	6½	14	C of E	Monogam.	Evenings	Shoemaker	0
	8. Alima	F	1½	6	Moslem	Polygam.	Always	Moslem school teacher	2
	9. Aida	F	2	8½	Moslem	Monogam.(?)	Occ.	?	9
	10. William	M	3½	10½	C of E	Monogam.	Occ.	Vet. Off. ?	0
	11. Senkumba	M	2	9	C of E	Polygam.—separated	Evenings	Clerk	0
	12. Kyimba	M	8½	10	RC	Monogam.	Evenings	Clerk	0
	13. Samwendi	M	2	6	RC	Mother not married	None	Mechanic	1
	14. Maryamu	F	7½	14½	C of E	Monogam.	Evenings	Farmer	0
	15. Lusiya	F	7	15½	RC	Monogam.	Always	Farmer	0
	16. Nabatanzi	F	7	14	C of E	Mother not married	None	Driver	0
INSECURE-ATTACHED	17. Muhamidi	M	2	8	Moslem	Polygam.—separated	Always—none	Farmer	2
	18. Magalita	F	9½	13	C of E	Monogam.	Evenings	Electricity Board	1
	19. Sulaimani	M	5½	9½	Moslem	Polygam.	Always	Farmer	0
	20. Nakalema	F	5½	9½	Moslem	Monogam.(?)	Always	Farmer	4
	21. Kasozi	M	11	15	C of E	Father deserted	None	?	1
	22. Waswa(1)	M	13½	21	C of E	Father deserted	None	Chief	4
	23. Nakato(1)	F	13½	21	C of E	Father deserted	None	Chief	4
NON-ATTACHED	24. Nora	F	5	12	C of E	Polygam.	Weekends	Surveyor	1
	25. Kulistina	F	4	11	C of E	Polygam.	Weekends	Surveyor	5
	26. Waswa(2)	M	3	8½	C of E	Monogam.	Always	Merchant	2
	27. Nakato(2)	F	3	8½	C of E	Monogam.	Always	Merchant	2
	28. Namitala	F	0	3½	Moslem	Polygam.	Always	Moslem school teacher	4 (sep.)

infants who sleep with their mothers (see Table 7). The mother is able to offer the left breast to her infant through the folds of her garment without otherwise baring herself. Only one mother ever offered the infant both breasts during our visits, and some were too diffident to feed the infant at all in our presence.

It was customary for all children in these villages to attend school as soon as they became of school-age, and although many of the children attended local schools and returned in late afternoon, some of the older children attended boarding schools. Consequently, except during school holidays, the only children home during the day were under six years old. Many of the mothers complained that they, therefore, had no one to leave the young children with if they wanted or needed to go anywhere that they could not be taken along – hence the difficulties of getting to a clinic or hospital.

The sample

The sample includes families from the three major religious groups in Buganda (the province of Uganda inhabited by the Ganda) – Church of England, Roman Catholic and Moslem (see Table 5). On the whole the Moslems are less acculturated than the others. They are also of interest in that some of them were polygamous, although it may be noted that polygamy also occurred in two households which were at least nominally Church of England.

The marital situations of the parents in the sample included not only seemingly stable monogamous or polygamous unions, but also unmarried mothers, women deserted by their husbands and left destitute, and women who had taken the initiative in separating themselves from their husbands and going home to live with their own families (see Table 5).

In all there were 28 babies, and 26 mothers, since there were two sets of twins in the sample. We visited 24 households, since in two of the polygamous households there were two infants to be observed. In most instances the subject was the mother's first or second child, although some of the babies had four or more siblings, not all of whom were living at home because of schooling or the custom of separation. Some of the households included children of relatives who were being reared apart from their families, or sent to attend the local school.

A few of the households consisted only of mother, young children

72

and father when he was at home. In others there were other adults and older children, who could and often did share in the care of the infant. In Table 6 we show the regular caretakers each child had other than the mother.

TABLE 6

Care from mother and other caretakers

Name	Ratings			Regular caretakers (other than mother)
	Am't mother's care	Mother as informant	Total care	
SECURE-ATTACHED				
1. Paulo	7	7	7	None
2. Sembajwe	7	7	7	None
3. Juko	7	4	7	None
4. Senvuma	5	—	7	None
5. Petero	6	7	6	None
6. Mutebe	5	6	7	MGM, MGF, MGGM
7. Nakiku	5	5	7	F, 1 Ch.
8. Alima	5	5	7	PGM, O/W, F, 2 Ch.
9. Aida	4	7	6	MGM, MA, 2 Ch. Neighbours
10. William	4	7	6	1 to 6 Ch.
11. Senkumba	4	7	5	O/W, F, Neighbour
12. Kyimba	4	6	6	PGM
13. Samwendi	4	5	6	MA, 1 Ch.
14. Maryamu	4	4	5	F, 1 Ch.
15. Lusiya	4	4	5	PA, 1 Ch.
16. Nabatanzi	3	7	7	MGM, MA, 1 Ch.
INSECURE-ATTACHED				
17. Muhamidi	7	4	7	None
18. Magalita	4	7	6	F, 2 Adults, 1 Ch.
19. Sulaimani	4	5	2	F, MGM, Neighbour
20. Nakalema	4	2	7	F, PU, 4 Ch.
21. Kasozi	3	6	4	Neighbour
22. Waswa(1)	3	5	6	2 Adults, 3 Ch.
23. Nakato(1)	3	5	6	2 Adults, 3 Ch.
NON-ATTACHED				
24. Nora	2	4	2	O/W; 4 Ch.
25. Kulistina	2	3	2	O/W; 4 Ch.
26. Waswa(2)	1	1	2	F, 2 Ch.
27. Nakato(2)	1	1	2	F, 2 Ch.
28. Namitala	2	3	6	O/W, F, PGM, 2 Ch.

TABLE 7

Facts about feeding

	Name	Method of feeding*	Night feedings	Mother's attitude to breast feeding	Adequacy of milk supply	Sleeps with mother	Weaning
SECURE-ATTACHED	1. Paulo	D, (C)	3–4	Much enjoys	Good	No	
	2. Sembajwe	D, C	3	Enjoys	Good	No	21 mos.
	3. Juko	D, C	1	Enjoys	Failing 7 mos.	No	
	4. Senvuma	D, C	?	Enjoys	Good	?	10 mos. abrupt
	5. Petero	D, C	2–3	Enjoys	Failing 7 mos.	No	
	6. Mutebe	D, (C)	3–4	Enjoyed at first	Good	to 6 mos.	
	7. Nakiku	SF	2	Enjoys	Good	No	12 mos.
	8. Alima	D	3	Enjoys	Failing 2 mos.	to 2 mos.	
	9. Aida	D	1–3	Enjoys	Failing 3 mos.	Yes	
	10. William	SF	2(Sch)	Duty†	Good	No	
	11. Senkumba	SF	2	Duty	Failing 7 mos.	to 2 mos.	
	12. Kyimba	D, (C)	2–3	Enjoyed at first	Failed 7½ mos.	till weaned	7½ mos.
	13. Samwendi	D, C	3	Enjoys	Failing 3 mos.	Yes	
	14. Maryamu	SR	1–2	Enjoys	Failed 8½ mos.	No	8½ mos.
	15. Lusiya	D, (C)	3	Enjoys	Good	till weaned	11½ mos.
	16. Nabatanzi	D	2	Enjoys	Good	No	13 mos.
INSECURE-ATTACHED	17. Muhamidi	D, C	5	Enjoyed at first	Failing 6 mos.	Yes	
	18. Magalita	D	2	Duty	Insufficient	to 4 mos.	
	19. Sulaimani	D	often	Duty	Good	No	
	20. Nakalema	D, C	2–3	Enjoys	Failing 6 mos.	to 6 mos.	
	21. Kasozi	D, (C)	2–3	Duty†	Good	till weaned	13½ mos.
	22. Waswa(1)	SF	2	Enjoyed at first	Insufficient	No	
	23. Nakato(1)	SF	2	Enjoyed at first	Insufficient	No	
NON-ATTACHED	24. Nora	SF	0–1	Duty	Good	No	11 mos.
	25. Kulistina	SB	1	Enjoyed at first	None	No	3 days
	26. Waswa(2)	D?	0	No reply	Failing 4 mos.	No	
	27. Nakato(2)	D?	0	No reply	Failing 4 mos.	No	
	28. Namitala	D, C	1–2	Enjoys	Failing 8 wks.	No	

* D—demand; C—comfort; (C)—comfort with some qualification; SF—flexible schedule; SR—rigid schedule; SB—bottle fed by schedule.

† These mothers implied that breast-feeding was a duty made pleasant by affection for the child.

Procedure

Each family was visited at intervals of approximately two weeks, over a median period of seven months, each visit lasting about two hours. Brief visits were made at more frequent intervals to arrange appointments and maintain contact. Data were obtained both through interview with the mother, largely mediated by an interpreter, and by direct observation of the behaviour of mother and child as it occurred in the course of the visit. I found that the pauses that were inevitable in working through an interpreter gave me invaluable time for note-taking. The collection of information was guided by an interview schedule, so that a uniform core of comparable information could be obtained from each mother. The schedule was not in evidence during the visit, and open-ended questions were used as much as possible and spontaneous conversation was encouraged.

Results

Although a good deal of interview time was spent in inquiring about current customs of Ganda infant care, it is proposed to report only those that seemed particularly related to the development of the infant-mother tie, and to defer discussion of these customs and practices until after having presented our findings about patterns of attachment behaviour and the developmental sequence in which they emerge.

Patterns of attachment behaviour

Twenty-three of the infants developed a clear-cut attachment to the mother during the period of observation, while five did not. For the baby to be judged attached to his mother he had to demonstrate that he discriminated her from other people and responded to her differently. Within the first three months of life, smiling, vocalization and crying could be observed as social responses, but they were not considered to indicate attachment unless the response to the mother differed in quality or in quantity from the response to other people. Thus the eight week old baby tends to cry when put down and to cease crying when picked up, but if this occurs regardless of who it is who picks him up or puts him down, his response is undiscriminating and hence is not considered to indicate attachment.

The judgement that the infant had formed an attachment to his mother as a special person rested on no single criterion; on the contrary, there is a variety of behaviour patterns that may be used as criteria of attachment. To some of these we were alert from the beginning, for example, the child's response to brief separation from the mother by crying or following when she left the room. Some children, however, who seemed obviously attached to their mothers did not protest brief separations, but rather showed their attachment in other ways. Thus our attention was drawn to a broader range of attachment patterns than we were originally set to observe. Our observation of these additional patterns was not as systematic and careful as it would have been had they been considered criteria of attachment from the outset.

Let us now list the patterns of attachment behaviour as they have emerged from this study. The first three patterns imply little more than discrimination of the mother from other people and differential responsiveness to her.

1. *Differential crying*

The baby cries when held by a person other than the mother and stops when taken by the mother; or he is crying and continues to cry when someone else attempts to comfort him but stops crying immediately when taken by his mother. This was observed in one child as early as eight weeks and seemed common at twelve weeks. At this early age, however, it was impossible to judge how much the crying was a demand for the mother as a special person, and how much it was a demand for the breast, for usually the mother's first act after picking up the crying child was to give him the breast.

2. *Differential smiling*

The baby smiles more readily and more frequently in interaction with his mother than in interaction with other people. We did not plan at the outset to make systematic observations of differential smiling, and hence it is difficult to say how early it emerged, and with what consistency the attached infants manifested differential smiling. In one nine week old infant, however, it was marked enough to be noted, but it was more regularly observed in babies of 32 weeks and older.

76

3. *Differential vocalization*

The baby vocalizes more readily and more frequently in interaction with his mother than in interaction with other people. The youngest child who manifested differential vocalization markedly enough to draw the phenomenon to our attention was 20 weeks old.

The next group of patterns have in common a concern on the part of the infant for the whereabouts of his mother – a concern that implies the use of distance receptors, especially vision, since the responses are activated by the mother even though the child is not in immediate contact with her.

4. *Visual-motor orientation towards the mother*

The baby, when apart from his mother but able to see her, keeps his eyes more or less continuously oriented towards her. When held by someone else, he can be sensed also to be maintaining a motor orientation towards the mother; he is neither ready to interact with the adult holding him nor to relax in her arms. The youngest child in which this orientation was marked enough to be noted was 18 weeks old. (The prototype response of following with the eyes undoubtedly occurs at a much younger age, but since it was not systematically observed it is not known at what age it may first become a differential response and hence an indication of attachment.)

5. *Crying when the mother leaves the room*

The baby cries when the mother leaves the room and thus departs from his visual field. If he had not been maintaining a visual-motor orientation towards her, he might not notice her departure, and hence would not cry until he realized she was not there; this response, however, is more ambiguous to the observer, for one cannot be sure that the sudden crying is indeed related to the absence of the mother. The youngest child who cried when his mother left the room was 15 weeks old; infants of 25 weeks of age commonly did so.

6. *Following*

The baby, once able to crawl, not only cries when his mother leaves the room, but attempts to follow her, crawling after her (or, when he is older, by walking after her). This response was observed in a baby as young as 17 weeks old, but it regularly occurred as soon as the child could crawl, which, in this sample, emerged at a median age of

25 weeks. By about eight or nine mon*h*s following tended to occur without crying. When the mother leaves, the baby follows her, but tends to cry only if frustrated in the following, either by being held back, by a closed door, or by the mother going so fast as to out-distance him hopelessly.

Even before the baby is able to crawl and hence to follow, he can take the initiative in making contact with his mother when on her lap or when placed on the floor beside her. There were two such patterns – scrambling over the mother, and burying the face in her lap.

7. *Scrambling*

This pattern differs from clinging in that there is no apparent effort to preserve a close and continuous contact. The baby climbs over his mother, exploring her person, and playing with her face, her hair, her clothes. To be sure, babies may manifest this kind of exploration with persons other than the mother, but they tended to scramble and explore most readily and most frequently when in interaction with the mother. Scrambling appeared as early as 10 weeks in one child, but was most commonly seen from about 30 weeks onwards.

8. *Burying the face*

The baby, whether in the course of scrambling over the mother, or having returned to her after exploring the world at some distance from her, buries his face in her lap. The function of this pattern is obscure, but since it was observed only as a response to the mother, it seems to be an attachment pattern. The earliest age at which this pattern was observed was 22 weeks, but it occurred more commonly after 30 weeks of age.

As Harlow (1960) has observed with infant monkeys and Arsenian (1943) with pre-school children, the baby, once attached to his mother, can use her as a secure base from which to explore the world, or as a 'haven of safety' from which he can face an external threat without panic.

9. *Exploration from a secure base*

Now that the baby is able to crawl, he does not always keep close to his mother, but rather makes little excursions away from her, explor-ing other objects and people, but he returns to her from time to time.

He may even go outside the room altogether, if he is permitted to do so. His confidence in leaving the secure base is in remarkable contrast to his distress if the secure base gets up and moves off on *her* own initiative. The earliest age at which this pattern was observed was 28 weeks, and the median age was 33 weeks.

10. *Clinging*

The clinging pattern which is so conspicuous in infant monkeys was not observed in these Ganda infants until 25 weeks at the earliest. The most striking instances of clinging in the first year of life were clearly associated with fright. We did not observe this frantic clinging response until after the child had become old enough to be frightened by strangers; perhaps it might have been observed earlier had the child been faced with some other type of fear-arousing stimulus. If already in his mother's arms when faced by a stranger, the baby clings to her tightly; if apart from her, he scuttles to her as quickly as possible and then clings. From the safety of his mother's arms, he can eye the stranger warily and without crying. If the mother tries to hand the baby to the stranger, however, he screams and clings desperately, resisting all efforts to disengage him. This frightened clinging in response to strangers was observed clearly in no child younger than 40 weeks of age. A less intense kind of clinging was seen, however, in somewhat younger children. One very anxious baby of 25 weeks of age wanted to be with his mother the whole time, and sometimes clung to her, but in an intermittent way, and not so desperately and tightly as did the infants who were frightened. Another child, for example, clung in the same intermittent way during a period of illness at about 32 weeks of age. Marked clinging was manifested by some children in response to weaning; this will be described later.

Finally, 'greeting' patterns seemed to be related to attachment behaviour. Some infants, who had become accustomed to being put down by their mothers and left alone to sleep, showed their attachment more by the enthusiasm of the greeting they gave the mother after an absence than by their protest at her departure.

11. *Lifting arms in greeting*

The baby greets the mother after a brief absence by lifting his arms as though inviting her to pick him up, by smiling, and by vocalization that might be described as a 'crow' or delighted shout. The youngest child in which this response was noticed was 21 weeks old.

12. *Clapping hands in greeting*

This response is similar to the greeting response just described, except that before (or instead of) lifting the arms, the baby, while smiling and vocalizing, claps his hands together in a gesture of obvious delight. After the child is able to crawl he is likely to terminate his greeting by crawling to the loved person as quickly as he is able. Clapping of the hands in greeting was first observed in a child 32 weeks old. In no instance of clapping the hands in greeting was there evidence of the mother having taught a clapping response previously, either by means of a 'patty-cake' game or otherwise.

In the case of four attachment responses – differential crying, crying when the mother leaves the room, following, and exploring from the mother as a secure base – the ages at which the responses first emerged for each child are known with fair reliability. The other patterns of attachment behaviour were noted only after they had become full-blown and obvious; their more inconsistent and inconspicuous early manifestations probably escaped notice. Nevertheless the results here reported suggest that there is a regular and consistent developmental sequence in which attachment patterns normally emerge. The sequential nature of the development of the infant's attachment to his mother becomes even clearer when it is viewed in the context of his interaction with other figures – both other members of his household and strangers.

Development of attachments

In discussing the developmental sequence of the attachment responses displayed by this sample of infants, each quarter of the first year of life will be considered separately.

First quarter

Six of the 23 attached infants were observed in the first quarter, although none of them before eight weeks of age. Between eight and twelve weeks of age, however, all did show some signs of budding discrimination of the mother from other people. Five showed the 'differential crying response'. The sixth child, who cried very little under any circumstances, made her mother feel none the less that she recognized her – 'by smell' the mother thought. As mentioned before, it was impossible to assess how much of this budding attachment was directed towards the mother as a whole person and how much to the breast. Nevertheless these mothers felt that their babies 'knew' them – that is, responded to them with some special recognition – although the basis for this 'knowing' is intangible, and was in this study very inadequately observed and analysed. One mother even reported that her eight week old infant knew his father, but she could not verbalize how he manifested this recognition.

However discriminating these infants may have been in the first quarter of the first year, they all tolerated being held and cared for by other people, at least sometimes. All who had caretakers other than the mother accepted them. All of them smiled responsively to strangers as well as to their mothers; in only one baby was the differential smiling response well enough developed to be noted.

Second quarter

Ten of the babies who became attached were observed at some time during the second quarter of the first year. The signs of attachment were much less equivocal than in the first quarter; all ten infants displayed some sign of differential response to the mother that could not be attributed to a demand for the breast.

Eight of them cried when the mother left the room. This did not happen invariably. It was more likely to occur if the mother left the child alone or with strangers than if she left him with a familiar caretaker; and even so it occurred inconsistently. Only one child tended to cry non-stop during the absence of his mother; the others could usually be comforted by other people. Three of the eight could crawl by the end of this quarter, and not only cried when the mother left but also followed; one followed even when left with a familiar person.

Two who neither cried nor followed when their mothers left them showed their attachment by greeting of a joyous intensity not given to anyone else, and one also by visual-motor orientation and differential smiling. Indeed, it was common for infants in this quarter to show a special preference for the mother by differential smiling and differential vocalization. Greeting responses were also common.

All of the ten attached children accepted attentions from other people, even from strangers – at least if the mother were present.

Even with strangers they would respond, smiling, vocalizing, and usually relaxing when held; but they were more ready to respond to the mother.

Third quarter

Eleven of the 23 attached children were observed in the third quarter of the first year. All but one followed the mother when she left the room. (The one who did not follow was ill, and, perhaps because of this, retarded in locomotion. He invariably cried when his mother left him, even for a moment, although he had not done this consistently in the second quarter when he was also ill.) Following was not an invariable response in several children, who were more likely to cry and follow their mothers if left alone or with strangers than if left with familiar caretakers. But they cried and followed the mother if they were hungry, tired, ill or unhappy. Throughout the third quarter following tended to become more consistent, as though the attachment to the mother were becoming stronger and more consolidated. Towards the end of this period three children, who followed their mothers very consistently, tended no longer to cry when following, unless they were frustrated.

Greeting responses, especially of the clapping hands type, were even more conspicuous during this quarter than previously. At this time, also, two of the children who seemed generally most accelerated in development used the mother as a secure base for exploration.

Despite the fact that the attachment to the mother became stronger during this quarter, the babies were still typically interested in other people. Those who had other caretakers accepted care from them. Those whose fathers came home regularly would greet them joyfully. All accepted strangers throughout most of the third quarter, but when about eight months old two children showed a sudden aversion to strangers, even though they had previously accepted them.

Fourth quarter

Twelve attached children were observed during the last quarter of the first year. These children typically followed their mothers, but they were less likely to cry when she left the room than they had been previously, and more likely just to follow – following her from place to place cheerfully and confidently. Following was not confined just to the mother, as it seemed to have been earlier. If the mother were not present the child tended to follow other familiar figures, other regular caretakers or the father. Two children, however, who were ill during this quarter, were less able than previously to tolerate the mother's absence and the care of others.

Greeting responses were more conspicuous in this quarter than previously, and they were extended by some infants to familiar figures other than the mother.

Fear of strangers tended to emerge in this quarter. Ten of the twelve were now afraid of strangers even though they had not been earlier. Children who had accepted us in earlier months now accepted us only uneasily and tensely, or shrank away. Children whom we met for the first time in this quarter seemed to be terrified of me – the white person – especially. Clinging in fright was noticed in this context, but in only six of the twelve children, and especially in those to whom I was really a stranger instead of an acquaintance.

Over twelve months

The same patterns continued on into the second year of life. The changes that took place seemed largely to be complicated by weaning, and hence will not be reported in this context except to comment further about clinging. Of eight children whose responses to weaning were observed, three who had been schedule-fed had minimal disturbance, but five who had been fed on demand responded for a week or even several weeks with a desire to be much more constantly close to the mother than before, crying and following whenever she moved away, reluctant to leave her side to play and explore, and in three children this was accompanied by marked clinging – clinging to the mother's skirts as she worked, seeking to sit on her lap and cling to her, and clinging desperately to her if she had returned after an absence. In all but two cases this period of anxious attachment gave way to a more secure kind of relationship in which the child was still obviously attached to the mother but much readier to use her as a secure base from which to explore and having less need to keep in frequent contact with the secure base.

Three groups of children

On the basis of these observations it was possible to divide the infants into three groups according to the strength and quality of the attachment to their mothers that they had developed: a secure-attached group consisting of 16 children, an insecure-attached group consisting of 7, and a non-attached group of 5. The children are grouped thus in the tables.

The secure-attached children not only manifested the signs of attachment to their mothers typical of their stage of development but also cried infrequently. To be sure, they might cry if parted from their mothers, or if particularly hungry, or they might be fussy during a period of illness, but on the whole they cried very little, and when they were with their mothers they seemed especially content and secure.

The seven insecure children, on the other hand, were said to cry a great deal, and they were observed to do so during our visits, even while held by their mothers. They demanded much attention from the mother, fussing while doing so, and they stayed close to her rather than using her as a secure base from which they could explore the world. Children who showed this pattern only temporarily, say during an illness or after weaning, were not included here if their long-term relationship with the mother had been a secure one.

The five non-attached children had not manifested any of the patterns of attachment to the mother (or to anyone else) during the period of observation. One of these, Namitala, was not yet four months of age when observations ceased, so she might merely have been somewhat delayed in developing attachment, and consequently will be ignored from subsequent considerations.[1]

A major consideration from now on will be to examine the relationships between variations in infant-care practices and the distribution of the babies into these three groups to see which practices seemed to facilitate the development of a secure attachment and

[1] Since none of the 'non-attached' infants was observed beyond 12 months of age, it may be argued that all of them may simply have been delayed in forming an attachment, rather than permanently incapable of attachment. The validity of this argument is acknowledged, since other studies, which cannot be enumerated here, suggest that an institution-reared infant, who has been unable to form an attachment during the first year of life because of insufficient opportunity for interaction with a mother-figure, may do so after adoption early in the second year of life. Nevertheless, the delay of the so-called 'non-attached' infants in forming an attachment is marked enough to justify identifying them as a separate group.

which did not. First, however, it seems desirable to introduce a few of these children and their mothers in the hope that they may come to life a bit.

Case summaries (see Plates 15 and 16)

Paulo (No. 1) was a very secure, handsome and healthy infant whose relationship with his mother approached an exclusive pair-relationship, although he shared her with two sisters aged two-and-one-half and five. The father was a relatively well-educated surveyor, able to get home only once a month. They had enough money to hire two men to help with the garden work, for the mother had no one with whom to leave the children while she worked. She was a warm mother, who gave Paulo much of her time, perhaps to the detriment of her relations with the second child, who seemed insecure, withdrawn, ready to cry, and who had a poor appetite.

When we first knew him at 28 weeks of age, Paulo could not tolerate being apart from his mother, so she took him everywhere she went. He was a vigorous baby, who made his wants known forcefully. When he wanted to be fed he did not cry, but took active measures to open his mother's dress and to get her breast for himself. At 30 weeks of age he began to crawl, and immediately followed his mother everywhere. He was also attached to his mother's brother who had come to live with them, despite the fact that the uncle took no part in caretaking functions, and simply interacted with Paulo, talking to him, playing with him, and smiling at him. Paulo also seemed interested in his sisters and would follow them while his mother sat visiting with us.

By 45 weeks of age Paulo was even more attached to his mother. Whenever she left him, which was rarely and briefly, he screamed the whole time she was gone, and when other people tried to comfort him he would bite them. He would not tolerate being held by us any more, and screamed when his mother attempted to give him to my interpreter to hold. Yet as long as his mother stayed put, he played happily, sometimes near her, but for a while out in the yard, scrambling about among the groundnuts that had been spread out to dry.

William (No. 10) had a different pattern of rearing, although his father, too, was posted so far away he could get home only occasionally. William was the youngest of 10 children, and there was also a foster child. The mother, single-handed, had reared all these children, grown their food and prepared it, made many of their clothes, and looked after a large mud and wattle house which was tastefully decorated and graced by a flower garden. She was a relaxed, serene person, who could talk to us in an unhurried way, devote time to playful, intimate interchange with William, and also concern herself with the other children according to their needs.

From the beginning she had attempted to learn as much as she could from the fortnightly baby clinic about European methods of child care. She found that scheduled feeding helped her plan her day, although she was flexible about the schedule. If the baby had been asleep and woke with a cry he got immediate attention. On the other hand, she expected him to settle down quietly after having been fed, and did not pick him up if he protested about being put down to sleep. She used a wheelbarrow as a pram, and there lay William nested amid snowy white cotton cloths. The wheelbarrow could be moved from place to place – out to the garden where his mother worked, or under the shade tree where the other children were playing, and never out of the earshot of some responsible person. The other children, even the two-year-old, were trained to fetch mother when the baby woke, while the older children, when they were home, helped look after him, and picked him up to attend to him and to play with him. They sometimes helped feed him the supplementary solid food that he received from three months of age and gave him his bath. He was never alone when awake, but by no means looked after exclusively by his mother.

At four months of age he was a happy, responsive baby, with an obvious preference for his mother, being oriented towards her and smiling at her, even when held by someone else. He began following at 24 weeks of age, crying if his mother outdistanced him, and, at 30 weeks, clapping his hands or reaching up his arms in greeting when she returned. He did not develop the complete intolerance for his mother's absence that Paulo did, and accepted his siblings' attentions with good grace in his mother's absence. Beginning at about 34 weeks of age, he had a long stretch of illness and clung to his mother more than previously; he became very angry with her if she went off without him leaving him with others, although he could always be consoled by other caretakers.

Nabatanzi (No. 17) was the child in our sample who came closest to having multiple mothers. Her mother was a big, strong, yet soft and warm young girl, who had produced this infant out of wedlock: she lived with her mother and her maternal aunt, having her own tiny hut across the yard from theirs. Much of the garden work fell on the shoulders of this strapping young mother, and she left Nabatanzi at home with one or other of the older women for long periods. The two old ladies were devoted to the child, but nevertheless the mother herself undertook most of her routine care, not only breast-feeding, but also her three baths a day and preparing and feeding the supplementary foods. She was very affectionate with the baby, playing with her, smiling at her, talking to her, singing action songs that she had learned in school, tossing her in the air, and generally enjoying her baby thoroughly.

We encountered Nabatanzi first at seven months of age. She was fat, happy and active, crawling about vigorously near her mother, smiling a lot both at her mother, at the older caretakers and at us. She was said to be attached to all three adults, and to have little use for the two other children in the extended household. She accepted being left with the adults, and would follow the caretaker of the hour. At eleven months of age, however, she suffered much pain from a severe burn on her foot. For some days she cried very easily and frequently; she cried whenever her mother left her for a moment, even though left with her grandmother or great-aunt, and continued crying till her mother returned. Shortly after this weaning began. The daytime breast-feedings were omitted. Seven weeks later the night-time feedings were dropped. Throughout this whole period and for the remaining month of our observations, she wanted to be with her mother the whole time, crying and following if her mother left the room. Although she accepted being left with her other caretakers, her preference for her mother was marked.

Nakiku (No. 7) was a secure-attached child, whose father played an active part in caring for her. He came home every evening from his work in Kampala, and gave the baby much attention, holding her on his lap, playing with her, and sometimes helping to bathe her. This was their first baby, although the mother had had another daughter before this marriage, from whom she was now separated. The mother was a quiet, slim, young woman and quite reserved. She showed Nakiku much quiet tenderness, kissing her repeatedly on the back of the neck or on the arm while she talked to us. These parents were

87

somewhat over-anxious about Nakiku's development, asking many questions about feeding, and displaying concern about her frequent colds and slow gain of weight. The mother used flexible scheduled breast-feeding, and was eager to adopt any other European customs that seemed likely to be good for the baby. She had obtained a pamphlet on child care, written in Luganda, and she studied this carefully.

Nakiku was never left alone. She was with her mother most of the day. When it was time to garden, Nakiku would be taken along and placed on a mat in the shade of a tree. A young boy lived with them, while attending the local school, and sometimes Nakiku would be left with him, or with the father when he was home; but she was never left alone.

Nakiku did not seem to mind being left with other caretakers – the father or the young boy. When alone with her mother she followed her about wherever she went, but rarely cried when following. She seemed to have a very happy and secure relationship with her mother – companionable, affectionate and yet not demanding. But from at least six months of age, when we first encountered her, she was said to have preference for her father when he was at home, even if she were tired or ill. When she was nearly 12 months of age weaning began. The mother cuddled her and comforted her when she wanted the breast during the day, and after three days she stopped trying to get it, and showed no further disturbance. Two weeks later the night feedings were dropped out; Nakiku cried a lot for three of the first four nights, and that was the extent of the disturbance. Afterwards she seemed to follow her mother less than before, and was more content to stay alone while her mother was elsewhere briefly, but she always gave her a warm greeting when she returned, and was responsive and affectionate with her. The close relationship with the father continued as before.

Muhamidi (No. 18) had his mother almost exclusively to himself and became very attached to her, but his attachment was more insecure than that of the other children we have described. Muhamidi's mother took him everywhere she went, and even worked in the garden with him slung on her back. She never left him with anyone else for more than a momentary absence. But she was an unhappy woman with serious worries; she gave us the impression of having stored up many troubles, and of being relieved to pour them out into ears will-

88

ing to listen. She had recently lost a four-year-old child, and her five-year-old had osteomyelitis, which, it emerged, was secondary to sickle-cell anaemia, and very resistant to treatment. This child was retarded, unhappy and unresponsive. The mother was also concerned about the baby, who at two months seemed a very healthy, attractive, responsive infant. Later, it emerged that her relations with her husband were also very unhappy; he expected her not only to grow the food, but to help harvest his cash crop of coffee, and she had no help with her two completely helpless children. She seemed to feel that her world was falling apart.

By the time Muhamidi was seven months of age she left her husband and went home to live with her own father, in a very complicated household with several young wives and innumerable children. Her own mother now lived elsewhere, and, although she was sure of her father's affection, he was busy, his wives were jealous of her, and she felt there was no real place for her in this household. There were other people there who could help her, but no one really did.

Muhamidi, by this time, had not only become very attached to his mother, and could not tolerate her absence for a moment, but also he cried a lot even when she was present. He wanted to be with her the whole time. When with her he wanted the breast almost always, fussing and clawing at her dress until she gave it to him. He seemed to feel most secure while sucking, and sought this solace frequently. He was an especially attractive baby, who evoked much attention from other people. He could respond to this when his mother was close by, but he could not leave her even to play. When he was about eight months of age his mother fell ill, and he would not be parted from her. He insisted on being in bed with her, and cried non-stop if taken away.

Even more insecure was *Sulaimani* who, like Muhamidi, came from a Moslem family. The childless first wife in this family was a big, overbearing woman. Sulaimani's mother was a slip of a girl, still in her teens. This was her first baby, and both she and he were unhappy. She had to do most of the garden work, but had no satisfactory arrangement for Sulaimani's care while she was gone. The senior wife took no responsibility for him. The maternal grandmother was willing to care for him, but Sulaimani had taken a great dislike to her (despite the affection that other grandchildren had for her) and cried non-stop if left with her. Sometimes the mother left him with a neighbour, and sometimes the neighbour's child came in as a baby-sitter, but often enough she left him in the house alone. He did not cry much under these circumstances, but as soon as his mother returned he cried most of the time. He demanded to be in her arms; the minute she put him down he would howl till she picked him up again. She would hold him till he fell asleep, and then put him down, but he would wake immediately and cry. He cried so much that his mother was at her wits' end, and could not behave consistently. Sometimes she was tender and indulgent, and sometimes she was rough and angry in the way she picked him up, slung him over her back, and rocked him. Sometimes she just let him cry and cry. Even at six months of age Sulaimani preferred his father, who, being a farmer, was home quite a bit, and he maintained this preference even though tired, hungry or ill. When the father came home mother had a respite, for then she could leave, and Sulaimani did not even protest her departure.

When Sulaimani was eight months old his mother and the senior wife had a fight, from which the mother emerged battered, bruised, in much pain and with a great black eye. The next time we visited, the senior wife had gone, and the mother said that Sulaimani was not crying so much any more – although she seemed, herself, to see no connection between these two items of information. From then on Sulaimani seemed more secure, at least when either parent was near him.

As for the other insecure-attached children I will only mention the highlights that seem possibly to contribute to their insecurity. *Magalita* seemed to have a devoted mother, but her breast milk had been scanty from the beginning and the child had also been ill much of the time since two months of age. *Waswa* and *Nakato* were undernourished and perpetually hungry twins. Their mother, with five children, had been deserted by her common-law husband when he was made a chief, and decided that he had best return to his first and legal wife when he assumed this position of authority. He contributed nothing to the household. The mother was very anxious and over-burdened, trying to grow food for the family and to find money for clothes and school fees. She had no money for meat or milk – the supplementary proteins that the twins needed. They were getting little nourishment from her, and yet because of the special significance attached to twins in this society, she could not wean them until the father appeared to participate in the customary rituals. In the meantime breast-feeding was dreadfully frustrating for the twins, and consequently a great anxiety to her.

Before *Kasozi* was born his father deserted to take a new wife. When Kasozi was six months old his mother established a new household with the help of her younger brother. She had to begin a garden from scratch. While she worked all day in the garden Kasozi was left with a neighbour. At thirteen months of age, after he could walk, Kasozi put an end to this arrangement by running away from the neighbour, returning home, and crying forlornly outside the locked door of his house.

Finally, *Nakalema* – it was not entirely clear why she was so insecure, but there were two plausible reasons. First, she had been ill a lot, and second, I suspected that her mother was rejecting, although I had but flimsy evidence for this belief.

The non-attached children present a more clear-cut picture than the insecure-attached group. *Kulistina* and *Nora* are half-sisters. The father of the family is a college graduate who has done well. The family lives in the best house in the village. They hired men to help keep the garden and grounds in order, and complained that hired help was less reliable and more expensive than it used to be.

The father had been separated from his first wife, although he was educating their children. He had acquired a second and third wife, with six and two children respectively. Kulistina and Nora were the two current babies. Kulistina's mother produced no milk when she was born. She was bottle-fed and did very poorly on the expensive imported preparations that were fed to her. By four months of age she was very malnourished, although she picked up quickly when the clinic suggested that cow's milk be tried. Nora had no such difficulties.

Both of these ladies, however, with the senior, Kulistina's mother, taking the lead, practiced what they believed to be acceptable European methods of infant care. Both babies were fed by schedule. Each baby had her own crib, in the room of her respective mother, and she was kept there most of the day, taken out for feeding and bathing, and produced in her very best clothes when visitors came. These mothers did not believe that a baby should be picked up when it cries, and these babies were allowed to cry for long hours, unattended. Eventually, they stopped crying. These mothers were both

91

very sociable and liked visiting. They acted as baby-sitters for each other, and usually one was off somewhere visiting, while the other looked after eight small children.

When we visited, the mothers dressed their babies in their finery and sat with them on their laps, seeming warm and affectionate to them. But they were most concerned with the role of hostess to the European visitor. It was difficult, with Kulistina's mother especially, to hold to the point of the interview.

Kulistina emerged as a very 'smiley', friendly child – indiscriminately friendly with everyone. Neither she nor Nora showed any discrimination between the mother, the other mother, or strangers, and neither showed any sign of concern at their mother's comings and goings. Nora was not so much ingratiating as independent. As soon as she could crawl, she wanted to take off to explore the world, and the last thing she seemed to want was to be held close by her mother or by anyone else.

The second set of twins, also *Waswa* and *Nakato* (the names indicate that the boy was born first and the girl second), were unattached. The mother had been married before, left her husband, and lived with William's family with her little girl until she married again. This time she married the village shopkeeper, and left the little girl behind to be reared by William's mother. She had two daughters by the second marriage, followed by the twins. Although having twins is a great distinction among the Ganda – to the extent that the mother is henceforward addressed as 'Nnalongo', Mother-of-twins – this mother found twins hard to cope with. During the first two or three months they cried a great deal. The mother decided to put an end to this; she resolved just to let them cry. By the time we began regular visits the twins were three months old; they were fed, put down to sleep, and then not picked up again until the mother judged that it was time to feed them again – regardless of how much they cried. The mother said that she fed by demand rather than by schedule, but under the circumstances it seemed that they were fed at her convenience.

This mother never once produced the twins for our inspection during a visit, unless we specifically requested it. She seemed pleased to see us, and was eager to visit with us, but she was most perfunctory in answering questions about the babies. We would hear one or the other howling outside, and later, when we left, we would see the father in his shop cuddling one or the other. But we never once saw the mother go out to investigate, or to pick up a crying baby. The mother said, with some pride, that she had never carried the twins. She had obtained a baby carriage somewhere, and there they spent their lives. We once saw the father kissing one of the twins, nuzzling his face against the baby's cheek – but never once did we see the mother perform a similarly tender action.

Perhaps, in time, the twins will attach themselves to their father. But by the end of our observation at 37 weeks of age they had developed no differential responses that we could detect. They did not cry when their mother left them. They could not crawl, so they could not follow. The only greeting they gave when someone came to them was to raise their heads as though struggling to get up.

Variables related to the strength and security of attachment

In describing the patterns of attachment and their emergence in the course of development, and especially in the context of the illustrative cases, individual differences have been implied – differences in the rate of the development of attachment behaviour, in the ways in which the child manifests attachment, and in the figures to whom attachments are made. Moreover, it has been implied that these individual differences are related, at least in part, to differences in the patterns of infant care, to the constellation of figures in the household, and to the relations between these figures.

In a sample as small as this one, it seems impossible to trace in detail the relationships between specific environmental conditions and the development of specific attachment patterns. Yet it does seem possible to search for the major variables which may distinguish statistically between the three major groups of children – the secure-attached, insecure-attached, and non-attached groups. It is recognized that such a search can result in little more than the formulation of hypotheses to be checked in future research.

With respect to some of the variables even this small sample is heterogeneous enough that hypotheses of positive relationships between infant-care and 'outcome' may emerge; with respect to other variables the sample is too homogeneous for statistically significant relationships to be found, however significant such relationships may be in another population of cases. Moreover, the search for a relationship between antecedent conditions and consequent behaviour patterns is a retrospective search. Therefore it has the strength of exploiting to the utmost the apparent relationships between antecedent and consequent represented in this particular body of data. It also has the weakness of leading to the *post hoc ergo propter hoc* fallacy in reasoning.

In full realization of these dangers and limitations, let us ask the question: 'In terms of what variables can these groups be distinguished from one another?' Both *a priori* considerations and the illustrative cases that have been cited suggest a number of possibilities. The variables that suggest themselves as possibilities may be classified roughly into two groups: those which are related to the feeding situation and those which are not. Let us first consider those which are not directly associated with feeding.

Degree of acculturation was one of the first variables to suggest itself to me, but it was abandoned because of the difficulty of distinguishing the relevant criteria of acculturation on any unbiased *a posteriori* basis. Suffice it to say that the mothers of secure-attached William and Nakiku attempted to put into practice the European customs they learned at the clinic and elsewhere, yet so did the mothers of two of the non-attached infants, Kulistina and Nora. The Moslem mothers, who in many other ways were the least acculturated, were the ones who used supplementary bottle feedings when their milk failed during the month-long Ramadan fast. It seemed to this observer that the mothers selected from among European practices those that met their own needs, and that the extent to which they were acculturated was in itself of little account.

Warmth of mother

On *a priori* grounds it might be assumed that the warmth and affection expressed by the mother in interaction with her baby would have much to do with how secure and attached he became. All but two of these mothers, however, seemed warm and affectionate with their children. The exceptions were the mother of the non-attached twins, Waswa and Nakato, and the mother of the insecure child, Nakalema, who struck me as rejecting. The others all seemed warm with their babies, holding them easily, seeming to enjoy the contact and treating them with apparent affection. So, for this sample, the warmth of the mother and her observed affectionate, contact behaviour do not seem to explain the differences between groups, although there is no reason to suppose that warmth would not emerge as a significant variable in another sample with more range.

Multiple caretakers

Although the first few secure-attached children on the list (see Table 6) have their mothers as the sole caretakers, it is obvious that other secure-attached children have several caretakers, and this variable fails to distinguish between the groups at a statistically significant level. It may well be, as Margaret Mead (1961) suggests, that multiple mother-figures serve as catastrophe insurance, and that the loss of a mother is less disastrous for a child who has been used to other care-takers than for one who has had an exclusive pair-relationship with his mother. Our detailed findings, however, suggest that a child cared for by several caretakers can, and frequently does, form as secure an attachment to one figure, his mother, as a child who has a more ex-clusive relationship with one figure. Indeed, there is nothing in my observations to contradict the hypothesis that, given an opportunity to do so, an infant will seek an attachment with one figure, the person primarily responsible for his care, even though there are several per-sons available as caretakers.

On the other hand, once the attachment to the mother has been formed, secondary attachments tend to be formed to other caretakers. It is interesting to note that several of these infants (we have cited Nakiku and Sulaimani) formed especially strong attachments to the father, although it was the mother who gave them the most care. These cases would suggest that child-father attachments may be significant even in the first year of life, and should be studied. This sample, however, offers no examples of a woman other than the mother evoking a stronger attachment than did the mother herself.

Amount of care by the mother

These mothers differed greatly in the amount of time spent with the child, in the amount of care they gave him, and in the extent to which they shared the care of the child with other caretakers. A seven point rating scale was drawn up to assess this variable:

7 Mother takes child everywhere; never leaves child with anyone else. Mother gives child much care. ($n = 4$)

6 Mother rarely leaves child with others. Most of the care given the child is given by the mother. ($n = 1$)

5 Mother is the chief caretaker and does nearly everything for the child, but the father or another adult shares in the care to some extent. Sometimes the child is left with others. ($n = 4$)

4 Mother is the chief caretaker, but the child is left fairly regularly with others for short periods while mother works in the garden, and others share to some extent in the care of the child. ($n = 10$)

3 Child is left with others fairly regularly for long periods during the day, but the mother gives child much care when she is available. ($n = 4$)

2 Child is left with others fairly regularly for long periods during the day, and others share in the care of the child even when the mother is available as a caretaker. ($n = 3$)

1 Mother gives relatively little care to the child even when she is available. ($n = 2$)

The frequency of each rating is shown in brackets after each item.

The individual ratings are shown in Table 6. It is conspicuous that the non-attached infants have mothers who received ratings of 1 or 2 on this variable, while it is also conspicuous that three of the four babies whose mothers received a rating of 7 are secure and attached. A median test shows that this variable differentiates the groups to a statistically significant extent ($p < \cdot 05$; d.f. 2).

Total amount of care

A case like Nabatanzi, who was secure and attached despite the absence of her mother for long periods during the day, suggests that perhaps the total amount of care may make up for limitations upon the amount of time the mother herself can spend with the infant. This variable was rated as follows:

7 Child given much care; alone and uncared for only when asleep. ($n = 10$)

6 Child given much care, but sometimes alone and awake. ($n = 9$)

5 Child given much care, but is quite often alone and awake. ($n = 3$)

4 Child cared for when he demands care by crying, and in addition he is given a fair amount of cuddling even when not demanding. ($n = 1$)

3 Child given care when he demands it by crying; otherwise he is left to his own devices, although not left alone for long periods. ($n = 0$)

2 Child is left alone in room a lot, but is given some cuddling and care beyond routine care. ($n = 5$)

1 Child is left alone in room a lot, and is given little beyond routine care. ($n = 0$)

It may be seen from the frequencies shown after each item that the majority of these infants received much care and were rarely left alone except when asleep. It is probably because of this very skewed distribution that the median test shows that this variable fails to differentiate significantly between the groups, despite the fact that the low ratings for the infants in the non-attached group (see Table 6) suggest that this may well be an important variable in determining the development of attachment.

Mother's excellence as an informant

This variable suggested itself as worthy of exploration when it was realized that the information we had collected about the non-attached children was more meagre than that accumulated about other children to whom we had paid fewer visits. A rating scale was devised for this variable, as follows:

7 Mother an excellent informant; sticks to topic, volunteers information, gives much spontaneous detail about the child, and never seems impatient in interview. ($n = 8$)

6 Mother a good informant; talks readily and sticks to topic. ($n = 3$)

5 Mother a good informant; answers questions readily but does not volunteer much information. ($n = 6$)

4 Mother answers briefly, volunteering little, but is co-operative, and has attention focused on talking of the child. ($n = 5$)

3 Mother a good informant at times, but seems more concerned with her relationship to the visitor than with talking about the child. ($n = 2$)

2 Mother a fair informant at times, but it is difficult to keep her conversation focused on the child for any length of time. ($n = 1$)

1 Mother a poor informant. Little information obtained about the child. ($n = 2$)

This variable was found to discriminate significantly between the three groups ($p < \cdot 05$; d.f. 2). The mothers of the secure-attached infants tend to be above the median in excellence as informants, and this is believed to reflect their keen interest in the development of their babies, which led them to want to talk about them and to offer spontaneous and detailed descriptions of their behaviour. The mothers of the non-attached infants tend to be below median in excellence as informants, which seems to reflect a relative lack of involvement with their infants, so that they preferred to talk of other things, and some had not even observed their infants closely enough to be able to give details about their behaviour. In this sample, at any rate, this variable seems to reflect more real involvement with the infant than does any superficial impression of the warmth of the mother's behaviour to the infant.

Next let us consider the variables related to the feeding relationship.

Scheduled vs. self-demand feeding

The type of feeding is listed for each child in Table 7. It is perhaps surprising to find that eight of 28 children, even in the villages of Uganda, were fed according to a schedule. Only one of the mothers said, however, that she went rigidly by the clock; the others said they were flexible and would neither wake the baby to be fed nor delay feeding if he seemed hungry. Twenty infants were fed on demand. Among these there were obvious differences in what 'demand' meant. Some mothers offered the breast whenever the child cried, for whatever reason, and clearly this was often a way of comforting him rather than nourishing him. Other mothers distinguished hunger cries from other cries and offered the breast only when the child was believed to be hungry. Demand was not necessarily expressed by crying. The older infants often took firm initiative in seeking the breast, crawling up on to the mother, fumbling in her dress, finding the breast and helping themselves. Twelve of the infants slept with their mothers, and for the six who continued to do so after six months of age, this clearly meant that they had ready access to the breast whenever they woke at night. Indeed all but one of the mothers who fed by schedule during the day fed the baby whenever he woke and cried at night. On the other hand, only four infants were always with the mother, even while she worked in the garden, and so the rest could not be fed on demand during the period when she was

98

working. Thus it may be seen that there was by no means a consistent picture of ready accessibility of the breast.

It may be seen from Table 7 that the schedule-fed babies are found in each of the three groups, and so are those fed on demand and those fed at least sometimes for comfort. When the 11 babies who were given the breast for comfort were compared with the others, the chi square fell below the level of statistical significance, although there seemed to be a tendency for this method to be used more frequently by the mothers of the secure-attached children.

Infant sucking

These infants were very rarely reported to have any difficulty with breast feeding. Two were said to have sucked very weakly at first, but within a few days sucked strongly. One baby, for a brief period when he was about five months old, stopped to cry in the middle of a feeding, then resumed sucking later. Otherwise all of these infants sucked well, some of them very vigorously, and none of them lazily. (In the case of the baby who had been bottle-fed from the beginning, the difficulty was reported to have been due to the failure of the mother to produce milk rather than to any failure on the part of the baby.)

Mother's milk supply

Some of the mothers had considerable difficulty in maintaining an adequate supply of milk. One, mentioned above, could not feed her baby from the beginning. One continued to breast-feed for at least 13 months although her supply was insufficient from the first. One mother of twins had an insufficient supply for two babies, at least after they had passed their first birthday. One mother became pregnant again when her baby was eight months old, and her supply suddenly failed. Five of the six other mothers who had difficulty were Moslems; their milk production decreased during the month-long Ramadan fast, and subsequently did not improve again. Under these circumstances they gave supplementary bottle feedings of weak tea with lots of milk in it.

When the 11 infants whose mothers had a good milk supply throughout the pre-weaning period were compared with the 16 whose mothers did not, the chi square was not significant. Insufficient mother's milk seemed to be important in contributing to the insecurity of the twins, whose mother could not afford to buy protein supplements, but most of the other babies did not go hungry if the mother's milk was insufficient.

In this context I would like to say a word about *thumbsucking*, which Margaret Mead (1954) states that she has not observed in primitive societies. Sixteen of these 28 babies were observed to suck either thumb or fingers, most usually the thumb. There were seven who sucked their thumbs a lot; six of these were in the secure-attached group. Five were fed on demand, and three of these were also given the breast for comfort. The mother of one of these babies had a good milk supply, enjoyed breast-feeding and gave her baby almost unlimited access to the breast for the period of 21 months before weaning.

Mother's attitude to breast-feeding

Thirteen of the mothers said they enjoyed breast-feeding, one of them confessing with embarrassment that it was so satisfactory to her that even though her child was over 12 months of age she was reluctant to wean him. Five said they had enjoyed it at first but now were finding it burdensome. Four made it clear that it was a duty and not enjoyable, while two more said 'I like it because I like the person I feed' or 'I like to do it because I know it is good for the baby'. One mother simply ignored the question whenever we asked it.

When the 13 babies whose mothers said they enjoyed breast-feeding are compared with the rest, a highly significant relationship with the strength and security of attachment is found ($p < $ ·01; d.f. 2). Twelve of the thirteen are secure and attached, and one is insecure and attached.

This is undoubtedly a complex relationship in which the feelings of the mother and the response of the infant can interact in vicious or virtuous spirals. Suffice it to say that 12 of the 17 secure-attached babies not only enjoyed their interaction with their mothers but had mothers who enjoyed at least the feeding interaction with them.

In summary, then, in this sample of infants three variables were found to be significantly related to the strength and security of attachment to the mother: (1) the amount of care the mother gave to the infant, (2) the mother's excellence as an informant, which was interpreted as an index of her interest in the child, and (3) the mother's enjoyment of breast-feeding. Two of these variables proved to be related. There was a low positive correlation (rho is ·37) between the amount of care the mother gave the child and her excellence as an informant.

Conclusions

It would be unwise to speak of definitive conclusions from a study based on such a small sample and using crude methods of observation. There are, however, a few generalizations that can be made tentatively.

It is clear that even in a relatively primitive society there are marked individual differences in methods of infant care – differences which seem associated both with the personalities of the mothers and with the circumstances of the household, and which seem to influence the strength and security of the infant's attachment to his mother. To be sure, this African society has been subject to considerable acculturation, but there must be, by now, very few primitive societies which have not to some extent been influenced by Western society.

There seems to be no satisfactory single criterion of infant-mother attachment. On the contrary, twelve more or less distinct patterns of attachment behaviour have been identified – and a more thorough study would undoubtedly enable one to distinguish more. These attachment patterns have been seen to emerge at different stages in the infant's development. There are individual differences in the rate of development in the strength with which each pattern is developed. It seems likely that these individual differences are related to differences in patterns of infant care. But there is enough consistency in the responses that mediate attachment and enough regularity in the developmental sequence to lend support to Bowlby's (1958) hypothesis of component instinctual responses as the basis of the child's tie to his mother.

One feature of attachment behaviour that struck me especially was the extent to which the infant himself takes the initiative in seeking an interaction. At least from two months of age onwards, and increasingly through the first year of life, these infants were not so much passive and recipient as active in seeking interaction. Perhaps the reason that four non-attached infants failed to develop discriminatory social responses was not so much that they received less motherly care, but that they were given so little opportunity to terminate their own attachment responses, being kept in crib or carriage, ignored when they cried, and unable even to follow a social object with their eyes.

Another feature of attachment behaviour that is noteworthy is that it is not necessarily terminated by a state of close physical contact between infant and mother. Some of the patterns do, of course, imply physical contact as an end-phase – differential crying, scrambling, burying the face, clinging, and also the attachment patterns of the feeding situation. Other patterns may seem to invite contact – smiling and greeting. Still other patterns, however, seem to serve to maintain proximity and the possibility of interaction without requiring actual contact as a termination – differential vocalization, crying when the mother leaves the room, visual-motor orientation, following, and exploring from a secure base. The implication is that however important actual physical contact may be to the human infant, many of the components of attachment and much important interaction between the infant and a loved figure involve distance receptors rather than tactual and kinaesthetic modalities. Even in infancy attachment can be maintained through a middle distance in which seeing and hearing of movement, gesture and vocalization form the basis for interaction.

This study suggests strongly that the infant passes through a phase of indiscriminate social responsiveness, to a phase of attachment to the mother, and then very quickly to an expansion of the capacity for attachment from just one figure to other figures – the father, other adult female caretakers, or even selected older siblings. It seems paradoxical that so soon after the baby can discriminate his mother from other people and after he begins to form an attachment to her, he becomes capable of discriminating between other figures and forming further attachments. As his attachment to his mother grows in depth and strength, his general capacity for attachment also grows in breadth.

One interesting feature of the figures selected for attachment is that these were sometimes figures who took no part in the routine care of the infant, but who merely played with him and interacted with him. This strongly suggests that something other than the mere satisfaction of bodily needs determined attachment to specific figures. It is of interest how early the infant can make these supplementary attachments, and how discriminating he is in doing so – rejecting some caretakers, and forming attachments in other instances to persons whom he sees with relative infrequency. These scattered observations suggest that we should not confine our interest to the infant's relations with his mother, not even during the first year of life.

It seems likely that, to some extent, different figures elicit different patterns of attachment behaviour. Thus it may be that the father or favourite older sibling, with whom the infant interacts chiefly in play, may elicit strong greeting responses. On the other hand, it is the mother, who is more responsible both for basic need satisfactions and for protection against threat, who is more likely to elicit protest patterns when she departs and more obviously serves as a secure base for exploration or a haven of safety in time of fright. Yet to judge the strength of the infant's attachment to his mother solely in terms of the intensity of behaviour reflecting separation anxiety would seem to be a mistake; some of the infants in this study who seemed most solidly attached to their mothers displayed little protest behaviour or separation anxiety, but rather showed the strength of their attachment to the mother through their readiness to use her as a secure base from which they could both explore the world and expand their horizons to include other attachments. The anxious, insecure child may appear to be more strongly attached to his mother than does the happy, secure child who seems to take her more for granted. But is the child who clings to his mother – who is afraid of the world and the people in it, and who will not move off to explore other things or other people – more strongly attached, or merely more insecure?

This study does not give any definitive answers to the question of the effect of multiple mothers or 'mothers-in-parallel', for in each case it was the mother who gave most care to the child even though others shared in that care. Under these circumstances the child tended to form a special attachment to the mother, if, indeed, he attached himself to any figure. If he attached himself to the mother, he seemed to be able to form attachments to other caretakers also, given the opportunity. If he did not attach himself to the mother, he attached himself to no one. There was no case, however, in which several caretakers shared equally in the care of the infant. There was no case in which the infant formed an attachment to someone other than the mother and failed to attach to the mother. In cases of 'non-attachment' not only was the amount of care given by the mother inadequate but also the total amount of motherly care.

Since all but one of the infants in this sample were breast-fed, this study does not help sort out the relative importance of the sucking response and the feeding relationship from other components of attachment. Nevertheless observation of the infants who were breast-fed over relatively long periods of time convinced me that the sucking response and the feeding relationship can be a very important component of the infant's attachment to his mother, and that the more initiative the child was allowed to take in the feeding relationship the more important it became. Thus the schedule-fed babies, who were permitted to take little initiative in feeding, showed less disturbance at weaning than the babies who were fed on demand and for comfort, and who thus had more control over the feeding aspect of infant-mother interaction.

With regard to the infant-care variables that influence attachment, it may be concluded very tentatively that those infants whose mothers spend most time with them, whose mothers are most interested in the details of their behaviour and development, and whose mothers enjoy breast-feeding, are those infants who seem most likely to develop a strong attachment to the mother – an attachment which is secure enough to enable them to use it as a base from which to explore the world, developing skills and knowledge, and to expand their interpersonal horizons to include attachments to figures other than the mother.

Discussion following Dr Ainsworth's paper

SCHAFFER *One of the issues raised by your paper is how one may best identify social attachments in such young subjects. The criteria you use seem to be rather different from those used in our Glasgow study of the same function, and as a result it becomes difficult to know whether divergent findings are due to genuine differences between the samples, or whether they are a function of varying means of assessment. You have been concerned mainly with the identification of the various constituent parts of attachment behaviour, whereas in our study we attempted to tap directly the resultant, i.e. the extent to which an infant strives to remain attached when his object is withdrawn. What seems to confound the issue in particular is the concept of security as applied to attachment behaviour. Could you say some-*

thing more about the behavioural distinction between attachment and security?

AINSWORTH *Babies classed as insecure were those that cried a lot, even if the mother was present. The secure ones cried only when sick, tired, hungry or left alone. Perhaps it would be better if I called them anxious rather than insecure. Anyway, I have tried to distinguish security or unanxiousness from attachment.*

AMBROSE *The relationship between these two might be quite complicated, since at some stages fear of strangers – and probably crying – may go along with a strong attachment to the mother.*

AINSWORTH *I agree; but I was careful not to use anxiety caused by strangers in classifying for security. As you say, it is part of the attachment pattern, but also it is likely to depend on how many caretakers the baby is accustomed to.*

SCHAFFER *I am not really happy about the use of words like security and anxiety as applied to early infancy. They refer to concepts derived from work with adults, and need re-examination in terms of this completely different age group.*

AINSWORTH *Perhaps the choice of words is unfortunate. I am using them as terms to describe two behavioural syndromes which seem to be quite distinct.*

AMBROSE *I am not sure that anxiety is an improvement on insecurity, since crying may be related to aggression as well as anxiety.*

BOWLBY *There is a measure which would seem to me to get at security rather directly, and that is a measure of the extent to which an infant will explore away from his mother.*

AINSWORTH *I agree, but unfortunately exploratory behaviour depends very much on age, whereas crying can be used as an indicator at any age.*

AMBROSE *If anxiety is taken as an indicator of the quality of the baby's attachment, one would expect the two to be inversely proportional since plenty of good quality care given by the mother functioned to reduce anxiety.*

AINSWORTH *My data are insufficient to make any firm decision on this, but it looks as if the amount of mother's care is a factor in attachment versus non-attachment, whereas milk supply, for instance, might be a factor in security against insecurity.*

GEWIRTZ *Given that crying is the measure of security, I wonder how a mother's milk supply would relate to crying?*

AINSWORTH *The secure-attached babies, who cried very little, tended to be given the breast for comfort whenever they did cry.*

GEWIRTZ *They were reinforced for crying, yet they did not cry?*

AINSWORTH *Correct. But I should add that it was this same group that showed the most disturbance at weaning. Children fed on schedule, on the other hand, had very brief weaning upsets.*

GEWIRTZ *You haven't said anything about toilet training, which one would expect to be a source of trouble between caretaker and child.*

AINSWORTH *They start training rather early, at about three months. The mother holds the child down in a squatting position outside on the ground, and she is careful to do this immediately the child wakes. If there is an accident, the mother is very permissive. I got the impression that training is very rapid. A child seems to learn more quickly that only one place, the bed, is forbidden, rather than learning that only one place is correct.*

GEWIRTZ *Are there any other potential sources of punishment?*

AINSWORTH *Chiefly after the child has learned to crawl. It is very easy for the baby to break things, since nearly all their belongings are on the floor, and also it's easy for the child to burn himself in the fire.*

BERNSTEIN *Do sex preferences show up in the mothers' attitudes?*

AINSWORTH *In this society babies are most valuable, and I could not trap anyone into showing a preference, except perhaps in one case only, of a woman who preferred being photographed with her sons rather than with the baby daughter.*

GUNTHER *Were there any special attitudes to the two sets of twins? I have the impression that mothers of twins frequently develop some hostility because they feel overburdened. The babies have to be fed in series, one cries while the other feeds, and the mother gets much less sleep even than other mothers.*

AINSWORTH *I had the impression that the mother of the non-attached twins was rejecting. Moreover, the mother of the insecure twins may also have had hostility underlying her anxious solicitousness, although she had other obvious reasons for anxiety – the twins' precarious nutritional state and the many problems stemming from the fact her husband had deserted her.*

WOLFF *There seem to be a lot of broken homes. Is that the usual state of affairs?*

AINSWORTH *I think it was fairly normal. The old custom was polygamy, and when a new wife arrived, the old one did not have to go, unless she was dissatisfied, when she could return to her family. Now things have changed somewhat. The father of these twins was made a senior chief and he felt he could not take with him a second wife with all her children. So he abandoned her, taking instead his first wife – his legal wife under British law.*

SCHAFFER *There seems to be fairly general agreement that two phases can be distinguished in the development of social attachments. At first attachments are indiscriminate, the infant seeking company in general rather than that of a particular person, whereas later he will require the proximity of some specific individual only. The time for this important change-over is usually, according to our Glasgow studies, around seven months. Even when we look only at your material on separation upset, this appears to disagree with your observations, doesn't it?*

AINSWORTH *I'm inclined to believe that the infants I observed were very accelerated in development, and Dr. Géber (1956, 1960), who has tested their Development Quotients, agrees with this. We both think it is the result of the tremendous social stimulation the baby gets. He is with people so much of the time, and can initiate contacts whenever he pleases.*

SCHAFFER *Could it be that some of the babies who were unattached at the end of your observations were simply late developers?*

AINSWORTH *They could be, and in that case they are grossly retarded in social development when compared with the rest.*

FOSS *You mentioned that one of the factors that did not correlate with security and attachment was the number of caretakers which each child had. In comparing this with other research, do you think it is important to consider how multiplicity of caretakers arises? When a child goes to hospital there is usually an increase in the number of caretakers, whether the child likes it or not; but in your Ganda children, there may be several caretakers because the child himself attracts them. The number of caretakers may be a result of the child's behaviour rather than a cause of it.*

ROBERTSON *In hospitals you have fragmentation of care, whereas here you have something more like supporting care.*

AINSWORTH *I am certain the cases are quite different. However, in my sample, I think the number of caretakers was determined by their availability rather than the child's behaviour, except perhaps in one case where the child rejected a grandmother. On the other hand many*

107

of these children make positive approaches to, and develop attachments for, people who do not function as caretakers at all. One chose an uncle, for instance, or there may be preferences for a particular sibling. In these cases it is very difficult to discover who initiates the attachment but usually play is involved in an important way. It often has nothing to do with feeding and bathing.

SCHAFFER *The trouble is that we have all carried round the idea that once a child starts making specific attachments he does so only to one particular person, and as a result we have generally not bothered to examine his behaviour in relation to the other people in his environment who can, potentially at least, serve as attachment objects.*

GEWIRTZ *I agree with Mary Ainsworth, that play may provide an important basis for developing these additional attachments. In our studies of infants in institutions providing total care, we have observed that a student children's nurse might make a pet of one of the half-dozen infants in her complete charge. The infant, perhaps as early as 7 or 8 months until about 13 months, might become specifically attached to her; that is, he would become almost totally oriented to her, he might make many responses or initiations which she would reinforce, he might cry when she would leave him or at the appearance of a stranger. While this process was ongoing, his object-caretaker would play with him outside of routine care situations and might, from her side, appear to have become attached to her charge, sometimes even before he would appear differentially oriented to her. However, not infrequently we were surprised to find that a student might make a pet of an infant who was not in her immediate charge, by spending time regularly playing with him, and that the infant in turn would acquire a specific attachment for the student. We could often spot this, because after not seeing us for a while the infant would suddenly take to crying at us, where before having become a pet he would have greeted us positively in his way. And we could sometimes spot the fact that the relationship had been broken (usually because of the transfer or completion of training of the student) by the fact that, on one of our periodic rounds, the child would again take to greeting us very much as he had before his specific attachment began.*

SCHAFFER *What still remains to be determined is whether it is inherently necessary for an infant to form his first specific attachment to one person only and then branch out, or whether he can start right away with several attachments.*

108

AINSWORTH *My impression is that attachment for the mother always comes first.*

SCHAFFER *My guess is that it need not.*

BOWLBY *Should we not separate two things: degree of interest in other people, and desire to cling to them when frightened? They commonly go together, but not always.*

AINSWORTH *And distress at departure.*

BOWLBY *We are back at the question of criteria for attachment. To put it the other way round, perhaps we should talk about attachment only if all these criteria are satisfied.*

RHEINGOLD *Do infants show responsiveness to particular people before they show distress at departure?*

AINSWORTH *Yes, this seemed true in my sample, although my observations of differential responsiveness were crude. Certainly, fear of strangers came much later than differential responsiveness or distress at departure.*

SCHAFFER *I thought at one time the two processes, attachment and fear, were complementary and directly related. The empirical evidence suggests, however, that there is no simple or direct relation either in their respective ages of onset or the intensity with which each is shown, and that they can really be regarded as two separate behaviour systems.*

AINSWORTH *I found distress at the mother's departure as early as 15 weeks, but fear of strangers came only at eight months.*

DAVID *We found this distress at the departure of the mother from an early age, but with no distress at the departure of any other preferred person, such as a sibling. Also crying when the mother leaves may occur when there is no fear of strangers at all. The two kinds of behaviour seem hardly to be related.*

AMBROSE *From my observations, there are two different sources of differential reactions to strangers. One is fear. But usually before that sets in there seems to be a reduced responsiveness which I would ascribe to habituation, presumably as a result of the baby learning that strangers are not as rewarding as the mother.*

GUNTHER *Could some of these differences be due to isolated unhappy experiences? My impression is that babies may develop a sudden fear of strangers from having been immunized by one, for instance.*

SCHAFFER *According to Levy (1960), this sort of memory does not start until six or seven months of age.*

109

HINDE *Can I return to the question of distinguishing attachment to the mother and attachments to other people? I want to ask if this is seen as a difference in kind or in degree. Perhaps I could take an animal example which breaks down the mother into her constituents, so to speak. When chicks are being reared by hand they form attachments for the lamp which keeps them warm, to perhaps the object they are taught to follow, to their siblings, and to the forceps with which they are fed. All of these attachments would normally be directed to the mother. The mother, in other words, plays many roles; and we don't know with respect to how many of these roles that deprivation results in distress. For instance, in Harlow's experiments, a fearful baby monkey will run to the mother surrogate which has provided 'contact comfort'. It may be that in Rhesus this particular manifestation of attachment depends on one particular role of the mother. Perhaps we should treat a human mother not as a single entity (the infant probably cannot) but as a complex of roles, and determine which roles lead to which kinds of attachment.*

GEWIRTZ *I would support that point. I think the word 'attachment', like the terms 'intelligence' and 'perception', is much too broad or abstract to serve as more than a label for an area of scientific interest. This label would cover the close dependence of the behaviour systems of one person, say a child, upon the stimuli provided by those of a particular other person, say a caretaker. In principle, many and diverse behaviours all might reasonably index, or be relevant to, the concept of 'attachment'; and as is the case for the many and diverse behaviours which might all be reasonable indices of 'intelligence' given the usual conceptualizations of the subject, these attachment behaviours need not correlate with each other in a simple way, or even at all. Yet these different behaviours might all be reasonable indices of 'attachment'. Progress in the direction of understanding 'attachment' requires that we attend more carefully under the theoretical formulations we have, however informal or preliminary these might be, to defining indices of 'attachment', and to examining empirically the relationships among the indices thus defined. For the beginnings of a social learning analysis, for instance, it would be necessary to discover which physical appearance and behavioural aspects of the mother or object person could serve to reinforce and subsequently to maintain a variety of the child's approach and other behaviour sequences, and to provide discriminative stimuli for the many inter-*

action behaviour chains which would be involved, and under which conditions the removal of particular stimuli provided by the object of the attachment would lead to crying, sadness, disorganization patterns, and like behaviours.

AINSWORTH *I would agree that different maternal roles matter more in forming attachments for some infants than others. In particular, for those children who were fed on demand, feeding appears to play a much more important part in determining attachment than it does in other infants.*

WOLFF *Mary Ainsworth in her report has drawn attention to the ways in which attachments are made, or fail to get made, in one particular group of people. It is a group in which there is a mixture of Moslems and Christians and where there are rather many desertions and divorces. A question we haven't asked so far is whether the particular kinds of attachment which are encouraged in this group will result in adults who are best suited to live in such a group. Perhaps the failure to form particular kinds of attachment (which we might consider important for Anglo-Saxon families) may not matter if subsequent relationships are satisfactory.*

BOWLBY *You speak as if we know what the significance is for later development of this or that kind of attachment. I do not believe we know it at all.*

AINSWORTH *In my thinking the concept of attachment does carry implications of health and non-health.*

THOMAS *It might be that the healthiest way of bringing up a child even in a polygamous society would be for it to start with a strong, single attachment to the mother, and only at later stages adapt to forming multiple ties. One cannot assume that because adults behave polygamously, infants should do so too if they are to be mentally healthy.*

BOWLBY *I agree that assumptions about the mental health implications of different kinds of attachment are likely to be premature. Is it not possible to use terms like secure-attachment and non-attachment simply to describe current behaviour, with no other implications? At the back of our minds we presumably think that attachment will turn out to have great importance for mental health, otherwise we would not be talking about it, but the form of the relationship remains to be discovered.*

AINSWORTH *Two of the babies in my sample, Paulo and William, are both in the secure-attached group. Yet the prognosis for their mental*

111

health differs if one is to judge from the mothers' behaviour towards the other children in the family and their response to it. William's mother distributes her time and affection among all her children. Paulo's mother devotes herself very largely to the baby, which makes the older children feel neglected and rejected. Perhaps this illustrates just one way in which the relation between infantile attachment and future mental health is anything but simple.

GUNTHER *There's another way of looking at attachment, which shows that it has an importance of its own, probably independently of the kind of society. Attachment is a two-way thing which is of the utmost value in survival. There is no doubt of its biological importance. Harlow's work shows that how and when the attachment between mother and baby is interrupted have a lot to do with deciding the infant's behaviour later; and it looks now as if a certain kind of attachment is absolutely necessary if a female infant monkey is to make any showing at all when she in turn becomes a mother.*

Observations on the Early Development of Smiling

PETER H. WOLFF

This report on the early development of smiling is taken from a larger longitudinal study on the development of affect expressions in which I observed infants daily for 30 (or 90) days after birth, in their 'natural' environment in the nursery, and subsequently at home. A detailed neurological examination, the observation of the delivery, and my close acquaintance with the child and its family through daily contact, led me to conclude that the eight children on whom I shall report were physically normal and that they were growing up in an adequate social environment, although the child-rearing practices which I observed may vary radically from what our prejudices may tell us is 'good mothering'. Whether the children I observed continued to develop normally after the period of observation I of course do not know; I planned no systematic follow-up studies, since the purpose of my study was to describe the ontogeny of specific behaviour patterns, not to describe individual differences. My only requirement for including a baby in the study was that the mother should have delivered the child at term, that she should be multiparous and therefore practised in her handling of the baby, and that according to the obstetrician's judgement and my initial acquaintance with the parents before delivery they should be, by superficial criteria, psychologically stable.

Because the obstetricians who referred babies to me practised in different parts of the Boston area, my subjects were taken primarily from two subcultural groups – the Boston Irish Catholic lower middle class, and upper-middle-class university students of no particular ethnic background. Once the parents agreed to the general plan of my study, I visited them several times before the delivery to let them and the other children get acquainted with me, to explain my interests in more specific terms, to assure the parents that my interests were primarily in the new baby, so that they should go about their business exactly as if I were not present.

I attended the delivery, and every day thereafter while the baby remained in the nursery I made systematic observations and semi-quantitative experiments. When mother and baby left the hospital to go home I also began my regular visits to the home. On five days a week for four hours and on one day a week for ten hours I made systematic observations, scheduled experiments, and anecdotal observations; the ten-hour period was my weekly occasion for making quantitative observations under standard conditions.

Contrary to my initial trepidation, I have always been well received by the family, with humorous scepticism and without any objections by either parent. Within a few days after I arrive in the home I am usually treated like a member of the family; no special arrangements are made for me, and by the second week of observation the family pays little attention to me. From the freedom with which the parents gossip with me and give me all kinds of unsolicited personal confidences, and from the freedom of family members to engage openly in the usual family squabbles while I am there, I have inferred that my presence is not a serious disturbance to the 'natural environment'. I do have some questions, however, about my effect on the amount and quality of care which the mother devotes to her new baby. In some cases I have observed considerable competition of the mother with me for getting the child's attention, especially when this involves evoking 'social smiles'; in that case it has sometimes become a contest in which the mother tries to produce at least two smiles for every one that I have produced. To a degree, therefore, my presence may speed up the social responsiveness of the children I study.

Since my sample of children is small (eight), and since at present we are engaged in a number of cross-sectional studies to validate those observations that seem particularly relevant for developmental theory, I will not deal with the material here by statistical methods but will report only on those developmental sequences and inter-actions between smiling behaviour and arousal state which I observed consistently in all of the eight infants, even though the precise time when a particular phenomenon first occurred varied by as much as seven days from one child to the next. (The calculated conceptual age was believed to be between 40 and 42 weeks in all infants. By

114

size, weight, and physical appearance there were no premature infants in the sample.)

From among the many affect-expressive behaviour patterns which were of interest to me, I selected the development of smiling because it seemed particularly pertinent to a study of the mother-child interaction. It is apparently universal among all infants in all literate and preliterate societies (Darwin, 1872), and in Western culture it is a significant communication not only between the child and its mother but also among adults. Although during the first week the smile is relatively stereotyped, it rapidly differentiates into a variety of subtle nuances; over the same period the internal conditions and external stimulus configurations that can elicit a smile become increasingly complex. What at birth appears to be a simple reflex movement caused by physiological conditions which can only have limited 'meaning' for the child, rapidly acquires a whole range of different meanings in the sense that complex and specific stimulus configurations can elicit it; thus it appears to become a 'psychologically caused' behaviour. A study of the developing smile therefore provides not only information about an important communication signal that establishes a social bond between the mother and her offspring, but offers clues about the larger problem how a congenitally present expressive movement acquires affective and cognitive meaning for the child.

In the following paragraphs I will describe the development of smiling from two points of view: first as a mechanism whose morphological characteristics and adequate stimulus configurations change over time; and second as a behaviour pattern that is sensitive to changes in organismic state. I have found it essential to describe not only the stimulus conditions, the quality of the response, the age of the child, and the past experience with similar stimuli, but also to describe in detail the baby's state of arousal at the time when a spontaneous or elicited expressive movement occurs.

This is not the place to describe in detail my criteria for assessing the infant's state of arousal or to discuss the more general implications which arousal state has for behaviour and development (see Wolff, 1959, Escalona, 1962). I will therefore simply list here the various specific conditions of the baby for which I made observations on the smile. Observations and experiments were made while the baby was in: regular or deep sleep, irregular or light sleep, drowsiness, alert inactivity (when the eyes were bright and the baby was capable of making visual and auditory pursuit movements), waking activity, waking alertness (only after the third week), and crying.

The first week

Within two to twelve hours after delivery all of the infants grimaced with their mouths in a way which morphologically at least suggested that they were smiling. The face in general is relaxed, the mouth stretches sidewards and upwards bilaterally into a pattern which strongly suggests that of a smile. The orbicularis oris and other superficial muscles of the mouth are symmetrically involved, while the rest of the face is relatively undisturbed. The circular superficial muscles around the eyes do not contract, and there is none of the crinkling at the corners of the eyes which will later characterize the smile. Just before the mouth stretches into a smile one can often detect a slight retraction of the ears, as if they were being 'cocked', much as an animal cocks its ears when it hears a strange sound. From the detailed observation of premature infants I was able to demonstrate that this 'cocking' of the ears *precedes* the smile, and is not the passive mechanical consequence of the mouth's stretching.[1]

In order to do away with the objection that such grimaces are 'gas smiles', I have scored as smiles only those instances when the mouth was pulled symmetrically upwards and sidewards and the rest of the face remained relatively uninvolved. I took this precaution, although I considered the measure unimportant since I do not believe that anyone has demonstrated that a baby will smile because it has 'gas'.

During the first week as well as later I found it necessary to distinguish between (*a*) *spontaneous* smiling which occurred without known external or systematically demonstrable internal causes, and (*b*) smiles that seemed to be causally related to external stimulation and which I therefore called *elicited* smiles.

I will not discuss in detail the presumptive evidence from which I

[1] Since this paper was presented I have had occasion to observe the same kind of smiling in a number of premature infants of 28 to 34 weeks' gestation. In these babies smiling occurs with great frequency, and whether the baby is awake or asleep, although the distinction in prematures is hard to make; in full-term babies, on the other hand, smiling occurs only while the baby is in irregular sleep and drowsiness (see Plates 17*a*, *b*, *c*, 18, 19).

inferred that certain types of behaviour (startles, erections, rhythmical mouthing, sobbing inspirations, etc.) occur spontaneously whenever the infant is in a proper arousal state, nor why I considered smiling to be one of these spontaneous discharge patterns that occurred specifically during irregular sleep and drowsiness. During some periods of regular sleep, for example, spontaneous startles occur at sufficiently regular intervals so that I have considered these to represent a rhythmical discharge pattern; each of the other spontaneous behaviour patterns referred to above has its own characteristic pattern. There is a statistically significant relationship of *equivalence* among the various spontaneous behaviours such that when the rate of spontaneous startles is high, the frequency of rhythmical mouthing pattern or erections is low; when the rate of rhythmical mouthing is high, the frequency of spontaneous startles is low. Spontaneous smiling in irregular sleep also has such an inverse relation to other spontaneous behaviour patterns – it rarely occurs when the baby is stirring in its sleep, and never within five minutes or more after it has startled. Particularly in prematures, but also in full-term infants, the smile may often be preceded by a twitching myoclonus at the corners of the mouth which has at least a superficial resemblance to an electrophysiological event and gives some further support to the notion that smiling in the early days after birth may be a spontaneous discharge. A final piece of indirect evidence for this supposition was the observation that like erections and spontaneous startles, smiling tends to occur with a high frequency at the precise moment during drowsiness when the eyes close; in other words, at the moment when an important avenue of sensory input is shut out, and when one might expect that a significant shift in sensorimotor thresholds occurs.

Smiling can be elicited during irregular sleep and drowsiness by a variety of sounds, but the response wanes rapidly (after one or two successful trials). Once the infant has smiled in irregular sleep, a refractory period of five minutes or more follows before it is possible to elicit another smile. In systematic experiments to elicit smiling I have chosen those periods of irregular sleep when the baby was relatively inactive and when its sleep had been undisturbed for some time. The types of stimuli included a clear, high-pitched brass bell, an Audubon bird whistle, my own high-pitched voice, the tape-recorded voices of mothers talking to their babies, and so forth. A single experiment consisted of five separate presentations of a particular

sound at standard intervals. The interval between the onset of stimulation and the beginning of an observable response was timed in each
instance. If a baby responds with a smile to such auditory stimuli at
all, it will do so only on one or two of the five occasions; and if the
baby smiles, the interval between the beginning of stimulation and
the response is almost invariably *seven seconds* (average range six to
eight seconds). If on the other hand the response is, for example,
gross mouthing or stirring, the interval may be shorter (three to four
seconds) or longer (ten to twelve seconds). Not all the data on the
observation of a seven-second latency have been tabulated, but the
preliminary data indicate that the seven-second latency is highly
constant during irregular sleep and that it is still characteristic for
elicited smiles in the third and fourth weeks after birth.

Any general comparison of the relative efficiency of various sounds
for eliciting the smile during the first week was difficult, since there
was great individual difference among the subjects I studied. Some
infants during the first week smiled consistently more often to the
voice than to the bell, while others smiled more consistently to the
bell than to any other auditory stimulus. Except for two infants whose
smiling was precocious in all respects, I observed no spontaneous or
elicited smiles during *waking states*. On a few occasions these two
infants responded to various visual stimuli with a smile, but I am
sceptical of the significance of these findings for the general sequence
of smiling development.

The second week

During the early part of the second week the adequate conditions for
spontaneous and elicited smiles in irregular sleep and drowsiness
remain the same as in the first week, although there is some evidence
of an increasing efficiency of the high-pitched voice. At this point in
development it does not seem to matter whether the voice is that of
the mother or a strange woman or my own falsetto voice – in each
case the voice now elicits smiling with greater frequency than it did
during the first week, and with greater frequency than other auditory
stimuli.

The significant advance during the second week is that the infant
now smiles with some regularity while its eyes are still open, although
glassy, immediately after the meal. The infant may smile spon-

taneously or in response to the mother's voice. Whenever in the second week I have compared the effects of the bell or the Audubon bird whistle with those of the high-pitched voice, there has been a fairly clear indication that the voice is more effective even during this drunken condition immediately after the meal; other sounds, however, are still effective.

The morphology of the smile also changes; the mouth stretches further than during the first week and may open partially; the superficial muscles of the cheeks contract, and the skin at the corners of the eyes tends to wrinkle, giving the impression that the whole face, rather than the mouth alone, is smiling. Since the eyes are drooping or glassy, the infant has the vapid, stupid, almost intoxicated appearance that is neither the grimace-smile of the first week nor the alert smile of the fourth week, and is a source of great amusement to the parents usually.

At first (eight to ten days) the smiling associated with the end of the meal occurs only within two to three minutes after the meal is finished; but by 12 to 14 days it may occur as long as ten minutes after the meal is over, and in some rare cases even twenty minutes later, provided the infant is still in this groggy, drunken state.

The third week

The first clear indications of a 'social smile' appear during the third week when a specifically human stimulus elicits the smile more consistently than other stimulus configurations. This specifically human stimulus is the high-pitched voice. Five of the infants between the thirteenth and fourteenth day, two infants on the fifteenth day, and one infant not until after the nineteenth day, responded to the high-pitched voice with a clear-cut broad smile while they were fully awake and while their eyes were bright.

The significant changes of the third week are: (1) that sounds are the first stimulus configuration which systematically elicits a smile while the infant is fully awake; (2) the human voice is more effective than the bell, the Audubon bird whistle, or the rattle; and (3) the infant smiles while it is alert, bright-eyed, and capable of attending (i.e. making visual pursuit movements).

This smile is radically different in appearance from earlier smiles. I have already referred to the fact that the eyes are bright and focused,

119

the orbicularis oculis muscles obviously contract and contribute the characteristic crinkling around the eyes; the mouth is pulled far to the sides and upwards and may be open, giving the appearance of a *grin* rather than a smile (Plate 20). Whatever the other morphological alterations of the third week are, the crucial change of the smile, and the one which seems to have the greatest communication value for the mother, is the fact that the eyes are not only open but 'bright' and apparently focused. The significance of bright-eyedness will become apparent in the fourth week, and I shall return to it in detail in the discussion of that phase of development.

To pin down what are the necessary and sufficient stimulus conditions in the third week which will elicit the smile while the arousal state is kept constant, I have used a battery of sounds presented to the infant in random order. These include my own voice pitched high and low; the mother's voice talking baby talk and making ordinary conversation; tape-recordings of other mothers talking to their own children; the brass bell which I have already described; the Audubon bird whistle; a rattle, etc. In addition I have compared the baby's smile to sounds when it sees nothing except the general surroundings with smiles when it sees a nodding face (either the mother's or my own).

Between 13 to 15 days and during alert inactivity the infants responded consistently to the high-pitched voice with broad smiles (closed-mouthed) or grins (open-mouthed). When I compared the relative efficiency of the various voice stimulations by testing how rapidly the child 'habituated' to them (the speed with which the response would wane), the mother's voice at this time was no more effective than my own high-pitched voice; the high-pitched voice was more effective than a low-pitched voice; while the tape-recording of other mothers talking to their children was in each case relatively ineffective.

All naturally-spoken voices were more effective than either the bell or the Audubon bird whistle, to which the infants tended to habituate rapidly.

During drowsiness and irregular sleep the interval between the stimulus and the onset of smiling is still between six and eight seconds, but when during the third week the infant smiles while alert, the interval between stimulation and response gradually shortens to an interval of four to five seconds, and rarely the smiles come almost immediately after the first presentation of the stimulus (one to two seconds).

Towards the end of the third week the baby sometimes smiles to an adequate stimulus (for example, a high-pitched voice) although it has recently been whimpering or fussing. Although the relative autonomy of the smile from the arousal state does not become well established until well into the fourth week, beginnings of it are already apparent. Until now the infant has had to be in a state of maximum alertness and 'relative contentment' in order to respond with a smile to the voice; if he gave any evidence of distress or indication that he was fussy, he did not respond to the voice at all except by a crying face or eventually by crying. At about 19 to 20 days, however, the first voice stimulation during a time when the infant is fussy will reduce the fussiness, and the second stimulus may produce a smile. After smiling, he will return to his prior fussy state.

By the end of the third week (in rare cases earlier), visual stimulation begins to play a part in the smiling response. In two of the eight infants the voice plus the nodding head was a more effective stimulus than the voice alone, while the nodding head alone still was entirely ineffective. These same two infants also smiled occasionally after they had been made to follow two objects alternately as each object was moved in an opposite direction. If at the moment when the babies were staring, a visual object was quickly passed across the visual field they occasionally broke out into a broad smile. I have called this phenomenon 'surprise smiling'; it could be elicited in all eight children by the twenty-fifth or twenty-sixth day, although in the two infants referred to above it was present as early as twenty to twenty-one days.

The fourth week

A number of new acquisitions are added to the infant's behaviour repertory during the fourth week which are all important for the further development of smiling, although they are not directly related.

The first of these, which is hard to describe in non-subjective terms and even harder to demonstrate by objective measures, is an apparent change in the baby's visual attention to faces. Within the first 18 hours after birth, the alert waking baby was able to pursue a visual object with co-ordinated eye and head movements so as to keep

121

an object in the visual field (see Wolff, 1959; White and Wolff, 1962). Until now, however, when I was looking at the child who in turn was looking at me, I had the impression that the baby was looking through me and focusing somewhere at the back of the head. At three and a half weeks approximately the subjective impression is that a radical change in the focus has occurred, and that the baby now seems to focus on the observer's eyes as if there were true *eye-to-eye contact* (Plate 21). I am hesitant to introduce these observations as evidence, since it is hard to convince others of the validity of my subjective impressions; I am, however, convinced that eye-to-eye contact is as important in the development of social interchange between parent and offspring, as it seems to be for all adult human communications, and therefore I give my impression here as tentative evidence. Dr Clementina Kuhlman is now engaged in a systematic study to test whether these impressions are valid.

Beyond these subjective impressions, some indirect objective evidence bears out that eye-to-eye contact may be a real acquisition of the fourth week. From preliminary experiments in which I assess the baby's level of activity while it is alert, staring off into space, while it is staring at me but I am looking at its ear or forehead, and while it is staring at me and I return its stare, I have tentatively concluded that eye-to-eye contact reduces the baby's activity most effectively. Three mothers who before the fourth week spent relatively little time playing with their babies, although providing quite adequate care, suddenly began to spend much more time playing with their babies and commented, 'Now he can see me', or, 'Now he is fun to play with', within two or three days of my first recording eye-to-eye contact. The mothers had no idea why they had this impression.

Eye-to-eye contact is relevant for the development of smiling because by 25 to 28 days, after the silent human face occasionally becomes the adequate stimulus for eliciting a smile, it appears to be specifically the contact between eyes that is effective. Although the voice is still the most efficient of all stimuli, and only three of the babies in this group smiled to the face at the end of the fourth week, in these three infants it was only after they had with a sombre mien 'inspected' the face presented to them, and had then focused on the eyes of the observer, that they broke out suddenly into a broad smile or grin. This sequence of events could be repeated many times: first the child searches the face, looking at the hair line, the mouth, and the rest of the face, and then as soon as eye-to-eye contact is made he grins. Other infants who showed the same behaviour later all followed the same pattern of inspecting the rest of the face before focusing on the eyes and smiling.

The second acquisition of the fourth week important for the further development of smiling is the progressive differentiation of vocalization. I cannot speak authoritatively about the details of this differentiation because I have simply described the babies' sounds rather than recording and analysing them by sound spectrograms, and the verbal description of sounds is notoriously misleading. Dr Eric Lenneberg at Harvard will soon be able to provide the objective evidence for the differentiation of vocalizations, since he is studying these by spectrogram analysis. However, my descriptions concerning the differentiation of sounds in these eight babies followed a consistent sequence of steps which lent my observations a certain degree of validity. At birth the baby makes a variety of sounds of which crying is obviously the most prominent. He also grunts when stooling, sighs in a characteristic manner when yawning, squeaks with a high-pitched voice in irregular sleep occasionally, and makes a variety of sounds when burping or spitting up or vomiting. (This inventory of sounds in the newborn is by no means intended to be complete.) In the first two weeks when the baby is distressed he usually begins full-fledged crying with some whimpering moans and groans. By two weeks he may occasionally moan and whimper for some time before actually giving way to crying, but the characteristic cry face is always associated with these sounds. By two and a half weeks whimpering and moaning, still associated with a cry face, are no longer necessarily followed by crying, and the infant may actually revert to a state of alert inactivity. Between three and three and a half weeks the moan and whimper are divorced from the cry face and occur while the baby seems relatively placid and content. At the same time the child acquires a variety of sounds deep in the back of the throat which occur while the baby's face is relaxed and placid. By four weeks the moaning and groaning are no longer associated with other signs of distress and are replaced by the gurgling and cooing sounds deep in the throat. During this time the infant gurgles and coos at the same time as he smiles whether the smile is elicited by voices or by other adequate stimuli.

During the fourth week smiling (*a*) becomes a predictable and

123

repeatable response to a number of specific stimuli in wakefulness; (*b*) achieves a greater degree of autonomy from the variations in organismic state; and (*c*) becomes the selective response to more complex and more highly articulated stimulus configurations.

In earlier weeks the baby responded readily to a number of auditory stimuli, but the smile was highly sensitive to variations in state. As is the case with a number of other well-circumscribed behaviour patterns for which the mechanism is functional at birth, the smile appears at first as a highly variable and unreliable response that is sensitive to variations in organismic state; within a few days after its first appearance each of the inborn or acquired behaviour mechanisms tends to become a more consistent response to specific stimuli and to achieve a greater degree of autonomy from internal conditions, while the speed of habituation of the response to repeated stimulation decreases. This progression is true not only of the behaviour patterns in general (for example, the smile as a general response to external stimuli), but also applies to the more refined co-ordinations between a particular stimulus configuration and a morphologically differentiated smile (for example, the bright-eyed alert smile to the high-pitched voice rather than to a bell or to another 'indifferent' sound).

Although my evidence on this point is not conclusive, such a progression (stabilization, repeatability, and increasing state independence) seems not to depend simply on the fact or repetition or on the amount of specific training of a particular sensorimotor sequence; other less tangible experiences resulting from the interchange between the infant and its environment play a significant role in this progressive stabilization. I make this assumption since the sequences I have described above are true for a wide variety of specific behaviour patterns (e.g. complex pursuit with the eyes, vocalizations) which could not all have been practised with equal vigour (by reinforcement in the conventional sense). I have assumed that the course of their development is co-determined by other developmental processes which are at least partly independent of training. Among these factors I would consider the increased capacity for alert attention to the environment, the decreasing sensitivity to visceral stimulations which until now have made peremptory demands on the infant's attention, and the progressive 'dynamic segregation' (Paul Weiss) as important. To assign an independent role to the *maturation* of

behaviour as an autochthonous 'cause' of development is as inde-
fensible theoretically as assigning such a role to reinforcement learning independent of more general central factors (state of arousal,
capacity for attending and expectancy, motivational factors). No
doubt different mechanisms of learning have to be considered to
account even for the development of smiling in the first three months.

For example, one kind of smiling that emerged first during the
fourth week certainly did not follow the developmental pattern that I
have described so far: at 24 to 27 days five of the children responded
with a broad smile to the game of 'pat-a-cake' when until that
moment they either had not been exposed to the stimulus or else had
never responded to it. Once pat-a-cake was effective, it became the
most efficient smile elicitor and remained so for the entire balance of
the observation period (up to three months). Infants who did not
respond to pat-a-cake at all during the fourth week suddenly responded with a broad smile and with high consistency during the
following week; one infant never smiled to pat-a-cake throughout the
three months of observation, although I practised the game with him
regularly twice a week after the end of the first month.

The game of pat-a-cake consists of covering the baby's hands with
my own hands, then bouncing my hands together three times in
rapid succession without allowing the baby's hands to touch, and
then observing the facial expression. To eliminate the effects of
conventional learning I have asked the mothers not to play the
game with their infants until I have had the opportunity to test it on
them at regular intervals. Since a number of mothers considered it
ridiculous that a baby should be able to smile to the game at this
early stage, I am fairly confident that no training by the mothers took
place.

Once a week from the third week on I briefly tested whether the
infants do smile to pat-a-cake, but in order to avoid any practice
effect I presented the stimulus only three times on one day of the
week. In order to ensure that it is the proprioceptive-tactile stimuli
rather than extraneous stimulations, I play the game in a way that the
infant cannot hear or see me or any other person during the test.
Using such a method, I found that between the fourth and sixth
weeks the game one day suddenly becomes an efficient stimulus for
smiling on the first trial, although before it was totally ineffective.
Thereafter pat-a-cake invariably invokes broad smiles even when the

baby is fussy, and it is difficult to habituate the response with re-peated stimulation. Instead, smiling intensity increases with repetition, the response latency becomes shorter, and the baby's excitement increases with repetition of the game. By the fifth week the infant frequently gurgles or coos with an open-mouthed grin to the pat-a-cake, and at times becomes so excited that its vocalizations resemble a chortling laughter (Plate 22). I have recorded these vocalizations and played them back to disinterested colleagues who, although they did not know what they were supposed to hear, generally reported their impression of a young infant laughing.

Once the pat-a-cake is effective when played in the standard fashion, one can also evoke smiling by playing one-handed pat-a-cake or by using the feet instead of the hands, although the response is neither as dramatic nor as consistent as by the standard method.

GEWIRTZ *How many times do you have to approach the baby with such a stimulus before you get them to start behaving?*

WOLFF *If they respond with a smile to the stimulus at all, then it is usually within the first but certainly within the second trial that I'm able to get the response. It was for this reason that I was able to test the babies in the earlier weeks without having to 'train' them by repeated trials.*

GEWIRTZ *You have a very small proportion of cases when pat-a-caking fails to elicit a smile?*

WOLFF *Well, I think if I gave you an answer it would be misleading, because I present the trials on so many occasions that I usually do get it eventually in most of the children.*

When we are talking about stimuli like the bell, the bird whistle, and so on, percentages of successful trials would not mean very much because it was in the course of these observations that I was able to define the necessary state conditions under which it would be possible to elicit a smile. Therefore earlier in the observations it often happened that I presented a set of five stimuli without getting any result because I had not paid attention to the state. Subsequently I was able to categorize time of stimulation according to state, and with such a qualification, during waking states even these non-human stimuli worked almost invariably *if* the baby had not been smiling recently (i.e. if there had been no habituation) and if there was no indication of fussiness while the baby was awake. As the baby gets

Peter H. Wolff

older it is important to make sure that he is not 'otherwise occupied' at the time of stimulation. For example, if he is looking at his mother or following a visual object, it sometimes is difficult to produce a smile. But as I said, the effectiveness of the pat-a-cake is so great that by the fourth week one can pretty much disregard subtle fluctuations in state. One of the eight children about whom I have reported, and one other whom I've observed subsequently, have not smiled at all to pat-a-cake for as long as three months. It is quite dramatic to see the fussy child changing its grimace from a cry face to a half-hearted smile to a grin, and then to go back to fussing and finally to crying.

AMBROSE *What is the longest period you have gone on with the pat-a-caking?*

WOLFF *I have gone up to sixty with a single pat-a-cake requiring three separate bounces of the hand against each other.*

AMBROSE *It would last about two to three seconds. Separated by what interval?*

WOLFF *Thirty seconds.*

AMBROSE *And response strength is about the same at the end as at the beginning?*

WOLFF *Well, yes.*

Doing it sixty times takes quite a while, and in the meantime there may be a change of state, so that the baby sometimes has gotten fussy before I am finished with my sixty separate trials. Then the infant may either smile through, or crying may take over. When he is crying the method is no longer effective for getting a smile. When the infant who has been fussy changes his grimace from a cry to a half-hearted smile and then to a grin, and eventually goes back to fussing, it is as if it were now stimulus-bound and smiling had become a peremptory response so that the infant had no freedom to react to his own inner dictates while being stimulated with pat-a-cake.

Early in the presentation I mentioned that I could put the baby into a state of 'fascination' by making it pursue two pencils simultaneously when presenting these pencils to the baby in the centre of its visual field and gradually moving them in opposite directions. Sometimes the baby tries to look back and forth and then simply 'gives up', staring in between the two pencils with a glazed look in his eyes. If at that point I pass my hand rapidly across his visual field, he may break out into a broad smile and at the same time look startled or

127

surprised. This 'smile of surprise' can also be elicited after the infant has put itself into a 'state of fascination', for example by staring at the wallpaper. If at the moment when the eyes no longer roam but stare, I pass my hand quickly between the wallpaper and the field of gaze, the baby is also likely to smile.

The necessary conditions for surprise smiling are that a hypnotic-like state has to be induced by prolonged directed looking, and then a sudden visual stimulus has to be super-imposed. My speculation is that this 'smile of surprise', like the spontaneous smile in drowsiness and irregular sleep, may be a mild electrophysiological discharge analogous to the spontaneous startle; the hypnotic-like state may be considered as analogous to a state of drowsiness, during which the threshold to spontaneous discharge is relatively low, the rapid movement acts as a sufficient trigger stimulation to elicit the smile as discharge.

With the exception of pat-a-cake, the most effective stimulus for smiling during the fifth week is still the voice; the mother's voice is now consistently more effective than the father's or my voice (high- or low-pitched). The relative autonomy of smiling increases during this period, and crying is no longer an absolutely limiting condition that inhibits smiling to vocal stimulation. When the crying baby hears the mother's voice, even though it sees no person, the first phrase of her talking usually arrests the cry; the second phrase alerts the baby; and the third phrase may produce a full-fledged smile. As soon as the mother stops talking the baby resumes crying. I have inferred therefore that the condition of discomfort (which is the cause of crying), although it persists, no longer precludes a smiling response.

During irregular sleep and drowsiness the high-pitched voice and other sounds are still effective and a seven-second interval is still the characteristic latency between the beginning of stimulation and the onset of smiling.

The increasing autonomy of smiling from internal visceral stimuli, and the simultaneous growing dependence of smiling on external stimulation, is well illustrated by my efforts to elicit a smile during the initial phase of a feeding.

Until now even the most efficient smile stimulus was ineffective when the baby was receiving the bottle, and if either the mother talked or I talked, he simply sucked on vigorously. By the end of the fourth week the smile as a response to the voice is sufficiently peremptory so that even during the first minute of sucking the infant may momentarily interrupt, give a broad smile, and then return to the nipple. He may abandon contact with the bottle to smile, or simply grin around the nipple. The voice (the mother's or my own high-pitched), without visual or tactile stimulation, is sufficient for this. It is easy to demonstrate that the voice alone is adequate since many of the infants I observed are fed by a 'propped bottle' as early as the second week after birth, and have no tactile or visual contact with the mother. Propping the bottle means that the infant is placed on a hard surface (usually the kitchen table) and turned slightly to one side, while the bottle is supported at an angle on a towel or a diaper (i.e. propped) and then put into the baby's mouth so that he can suck at will. Usually the mother picks up the baby every five minutes or so to burp him, but otherwise there is no visual or tactile contact with the mother (Plate 23*a*, *b*).

From these findings I have speculated that the internal visceral stimuli (in this case the component stimuli conceptualized under hunger) which facilitate sucking and mouthing at first compete with external stimuli of various kinds for the baby's 'attention'. During the early weeks the balance is generally in favour of internal causes of behaviour, and the baby behaves as if he were compelled to react to the inner stimulations, responding to external stimuli only when the internal demands of the body (the need to sleep or the motor response to internal distress) are minimal. As the peremptory quality of visceral stimulation abates, and as adaptive behaviour patterns specific to external stimuli stabilize and become relatively auto-nomous from internal conditions, the smile becomes stimulus-bound in a new way, namely to external stimulation.

The 'stimulus-boundness' of smiling gradually recedes during the third month of development, and the infant smiles more selectively, as if it were no longer compelled to smile each time it heard a voice. Thus the selective social response to external stimuli requires the development of a relative autonomy not only from internal but from external stimulation as well.

The fifth week

Before describing the further development of smiling, I will briefly return to the description of vocalization, which assumes a new significance as social communication during the fifth week. So far I have described how the pre-cry sounds became dissociated from crying as well as from the cry face, and were gradually converted into coos, gurgles, and a variety of other vocalizations; how these sounds no longer suggested distress to the mother, and were no longer associated with other behavioural indices of discomfort; how coos and gurgles became specifically associated with smiling and grinning, whether as a response to voices, pat-a-cake, or other adequate stimuli.

Between 28 to 32 days the voice alone seems to lose some of its efficiency, and the baby sometimes responds to the voice by simply gurgling or cooing without smiling. At this point it is possible to carry on 'conversations' with those babies, in whom the vocalizations have developed more fully. By imitating the baby's sounds it is possible to engage in an exchange of between ten and fifteen vocalizations. I have tape-recorded such conversations, nodding my head silently for five minutes at a time (which now can elicit a smile), then disappearing from sight and talking to the baby for five minutes; then again silently nodding for five minutes, etc. Such experiments give clear evidence that the preferred response to vocalization now is vocal reply, while the baby responds to the silent nodding head with smiling, which may or may not be associated with gurgling and cooing. The amount of vocalization the infant makes is significantly less when I do not reply vocally than when I attempt to carry on a conversation with it. This experiment was varied in a number of ways to compare the effect of the mother's voice with that of my silent nodding head, and the effect of my voice with that of the mother's silent nodding head. The mother's voice was more effective than mine for eliciting vocalization, but there was no detectable difference between the two visual stimulations in evoking the smile. The cumulative effect of a nodding, talking head is still more efficient than either the voice or the silent nodding head alone. The more complex stimulus can be made up of my voice and the mother's head or the mother's voice and my head. The mother's voice, either with her own head or my head, is still the most effective of all the stimuli I have used.

AMBROSE *Is motion essential here?*
WOLFF *At this point gross motion of the whole head seems to be essential. Within a few days after this becomes a sufficient stimulus,*

130

however, 'intrafacial' movements like grimacing, moving the mouth, raising the eyebrows, and so on, begin in themselves to be sufficient and one can then keep the head still.

AMBROSE *There's got to be movement?*

WOLFF *Well, grimacing or rolling the forehead or the like – at first, yes. Once eye-to-eye contact becomes a significant factor in producing smiling, then it is possible to keep the head as still as possible, making no grimaces, not moving the mouth, etc., and as I described before, as soon as the eyes zero in on my eyes the baby starts to grin.*

AMBROSE *With the auditory stimulation is there any difference between the effect of, say, talking, speaking, and a constant noise which isn't broken up in any way? Do you have any data on that?*

WOLFF *Yes and no. I mentioned comparing the effect of the mother's voice when she does baby talk and when she speaks in ordinary conversation to other people, where I found that the baby talk in some babies is more effective but certainly not in all babies. I have also made experiments with a constant random white noise which until about three and a half weeks after birth put the baby to sleep almost invariably and thereafter either caused distress or no response whatsoever. For this I have not used pure tones but rather a random distribution of all audible frequencies. I don't think that this, however, answers your question. I have not tried simply making one monotonous tone with my own mouth or asking the mother to do so. Is this the kind of thing you had in mind?*

AMBROSE *Yes.*

When the voice becomes less efficient as a smile evoker, the silent nodding head becomes the first visual stimulus that consistently elicits smiling (31 to 35 days). The interval between the beginning of stimulation and the onset of smiling may at times be seven seconds or even longer, but it is usually much shorter now and may be as short as two seconds. Several days to several weeks after visual stimulation alone is effective, the child will search the face, looking first at the hair line, then at the mouth, and finally making contact with the eyes, at which point it will break into a grin. When visual stimulation becomes the necessary condition for smiling the interval between the beginning of stimulation and the onset of smiling of course is much longer, and depends on the time the child takes to inspect the face intently before making contact with the eyes.

As with the voice, I have experimented with variations of the visual stimulus, comparing the efficiency of a latex mask of an American comedian with a large nose, the mask of a monster, and various sun-glasses with the efficiency of my bare face. Both masks have a hole in the mouth area through which I can stick my tongue to produce movement within the total configuration of the face. The nodding mask, the natural face with the sun-glasses, and the mask with the sun-glasses, are all effective for eliciting a smile, although the bare face is the most effective. I have never found the mother's face to be more effective than my own when no vocalizations are added. On occasion I have introduced into this experiment a stranger who has never seen the baby. His silent nodding face is as effective as familiar faces.

When testing the relative effect of various visual configurations by measuring the rate at which the smile wanes, I found that the bare face is in all instances the most effective stimulus and that it may produce as many as twenty-three distinct smiles in succession provided the baby is in 'a good mood'. When after a long series the baby no longer smiles to a face (usually after seven to ten stimulations), he will again respond with a full-blown grin accompanied by gurgling and cooing, as soon as I put on the mask. If thereafter he habituates to the mask (an average of five responses), the mask will again become effective if I add a set of sun-glasses, although now the response occurs only three, at most four, times. Removing the glasses again causes a brief return of the smile, and then removing the mask so that the baby sees only my bare face results in a rather longer period of continued smiling, when all variations on the natural stimulus have become relatively ineffective. The sequence of presentations can be varied so that the baby sees the mask with the eyeglasses first and the bare face at the end. This result is the same. The bare face is the most effective visual stimulus; whenever a stimulus configuration is no longer effective, some alteration like putting on the glasses is again effective; the mask is a more effective stimulus when I use the mouth aperture to stick my tongue through it and move it back and forth while looking at the baby.

In concluding the discussion of the first month I should emphasize that the number of subjects on whom I have made these observations is small, although the actual number of trials per baby is quite large and the reliability across babies is relatively good. About the sequence of the major steps in the development of smiling I am fairly confident; about the smaller details I will withhold judgement until we have observed a larger number of babies systematically. I hope Dr Kuhlman's systematic study on smiling to a variety of controlled stimuli will give us the quantitative data soon to show whether what I have described here is correct.

The second and third months

I will discuss the development beyond the first month only briefly because the number of babies I have observed beyond the first month is even smaller, and I will refer only to sequences which were constant from one baby to the next and partly confirmed by the anecdotal impressions of other observers who have described affect-expressive development.

By two months the three infants I have observed often grinned and gurgled 'spontaneously' while they neither heard nor saw a person near them and while they were engaged in what Piaget has called practice activities (primary and secondary circular reactions). While engaged in this fashion, visually exploring the environment, looking at their hands, or simply kicking their legs rhythmically, all three babies intermittently smiled and gurgled, sometimes smiling silently, sometimes gurgling without any grimaces. So far I have not determined the critical conditions that predispose to such spontaneous gurgling or smiling. The intensity or the direction of activity does not seem to be a decisive factor. During this activity the baby can be distracted to pursue a visual stimulus, and towards the end of each pursuit, when either the baby or I interrupt the test, he may break out into a gurgling smile. Gurgling and smiling are no longer necessarily associated, and the two behaviours now seem 'dynamically segregated' (Paul Weiss), to be used either separately or in coordination but are no longer indissociably tied to each other. The range of vocalizations expands rapidly during the second and third months, and the smile becomes more selective. The infant, although in 'optimal' condition for smiling, sometimes will not respond to the optimal stimulus. Towards the end of the third month there is again a decrease in the predictability of smiling; the incidence of smiling is no longer a function of either the arousal state or the adequacy of stimulation. But the configuration of the visual stimulus is not yet

K   133

the critical factor, and the mother's face, my face, and a relative stranger's face all seem equally effective. My observations suggest that when the baby is 'otherwise engaged' in some self-initiated task, he is less likely to smile than when lying alert and simply looking or staring off into space. Thus limiting conditions which were originally physiological (organismic state) seem gradually to be replaced by limiting conditions that we would call psychological. The infant responds more selectively; the competition is now no longer between internal visceral stimuli and external peremptory stimuli, but between the external stimulus and some internal directing factor which may be functionally related to what later become attention and intentional behaviour.

Discussion following Dr Wolff's first paper

GEWIRTZ *At what particular times do you test the infant? I know you observe the infant throughout the day, but I would be interested in the particular cues you use for his state or behaviour to determine when to present your test stimuli to him. Since you have reported that the infant's responses to stimuli might be relatively invariant under particular conditions, it is important that those conditions be specified in some detail.*

WOLFF *Yes. Let me first say that when the conditions for observation (the parents' schedules and my schedule) are optimal, then on five days a week I observe four hours each day, arranging my schedule so that the observations are distributed over morning, noon, and early evening, but never in the middle of the night, because the parents would not appreciate it. During those times I usually carry out anecdotal observations, some random tests, and I try to pay particular attention to new acquisitions that I have not observed before. One day a week I spend ten hours in the home and according to a pre-determined schedule test the infant by various standard means in the six or so states that I have arbitrarily set up to cover the variations in the infant's internal condition. Whenever a new arousal state emerges (for example, something like alert activity, which first becomes apparent during the fifth or six week), this state is also included in the schedule of testing.*

GEWIRTZ *Could you briefly repeat the seven states?*

134

WOLFF *By simple pneumographic recordings I have classified three distinct kinds of sleep. The first of these I call regular because the pattern of respiration is even and the interval between inspirations is regular. This is the state I have equated with deep sleep. The second I call periodic sleep because the pattern of respiration is typically periodic and sometimes approaches Cheyne-Stokes respiration. And the third state I call irregular sleep, which I have identified with light sleep. Periodic sleep is in most respects an in-between level, lighter than deep sleep and deeper than irregular sleep. Next is a state I call drowsiness, in which the baby is relatively inactive, its eyes are glassy, opening and closing intermittently, and there is relatively little response to the environment although the baby is very sensitive to vestibular stimulations and startles very easily. Then the state of alert inactivity is a condition in which the eyes are bright, activity is relatively low, the infant is insensitive to vestibular stimulation and able to make rather persistent visual and auditory pursuit movements. For the period of the first month after birth, the next state in this continuum of arousal levels is what I have called waking activity; the baby is motorically active, not crying although he may be grimacing, and he does not make visual pursuit movements or engage in other adaptive behaviours which require some kind of interchange with concrete objects in the environment. By four weeks at the earliest, but usually by six weeks, an apparently new level of arousal emerges which I have called alert activity, because the baby can now engage in rhythmical motor actions and at the same time make visual and other adaptive pursuit movements.*

SCHAFFER *Such prolonged observations – four hours a day, sometimes ten hours – must have meant that these babies were exposed to quite an unusually large amount of stimulation. Presumably, though you were not directly interacting with them all the time, you were continually in their visual field. I mention this because of the age which you give for visual pursuit activities. This is very much earlier than given by the usual developmental norms.*

WOLFF *You mean learning by 18 hours? I would hardly think that the visual pursuit of the newborn at this point is due to social stimulation. As a matter of fact, in some instances it is possible to get not only visual but also auditory pursuit movements within the first few hours after birth, provided that the infant is in its optimal state of alert inactivity. I just believe that the infant is congenitally* equipped to make pursuit movements, to smile, and that people have simply not paid attention to the organismic state when they have tried to elicit these responses in the newborn. By 'congenitally' I mean nothing more than that it is present at birth, and I don't believe one has to take either an extreme or a compromise position on whether this is hereditary or learned before birth. If the baby has not been heavily anaesthetized you can get visual pursuit movements within the first two hours, and by 18 hours it will pursue the visual stimulus not only with the eyes but also with the head. This, I believe, cannot be the result of social stimulation.

Concerning the effect of my presence on later social responses, it seems quite possible that my presence has a practice effect and that all the figures I've given you are somewhat precocious. Furthermore in some cases the mother certainly compounds the difficulty by competing with me. In order to cut down this practice effect I try to do systematic testing only once a week and as little as possible on other days during the week. Certainly when I am not testing I stay out of the child's view as much as possible in a way that allows me to see what the child and its face are doing without the child seeing me.

RHEINGOLD *If your infants are advanced in visual and adaptive pursuit movements, then you have evidence of the effects of early stimulation and, hence, of learning.*

WOLFF *I would question that. I would say that maybe it comes earlier, but using the term 'learning' in its conventional sense (e.g. operant conditioning) conveys a great deal more than I would care to say.*

RHEINGOLD *Well, you would have to account somehow for the effect of the additional experience, customarily called learning.*

WOLFF *For us, learning is a dirty word. I should say again, however, that I have to be very careful about making general claims, because much of my material comes from one subcultural group about whose child-rearing practices I have collected a great deal of data. This is the Boston Irish, and my impression so far is that the parents here like to play with their children a good deal; it is also in this group that I find the responsiveness so early. In other subjects – for example, the children of Harvard College graduates – the onset of smiling is not as precocious, although there I am playing with the child at least as much as in the homes of the Boston Irish. I do believe there is something different about the social responsiveness in the children*

136

of the two groups, but I hesitate to say what. I didn't make any remarks about individual differences because I think (1) my sample is too small and (2) the developmental processes of smiling itself and the epigenetic series have to be described before we can study individual differences and the effect of variations in the environment on this process.

GUNTHER *Can I ask about the relation to term? Were they sometimes ten days after term of delivery and sometimes ten days before, or were all yours rather hurried along at the right day?*

WOLFF *The ones I am reporting here include only one post-mature baby in whom, however, the amniotic fluid was not stained. This baby was post-mature only by calculation. To the best of my knowledge and that of the obstetricians the rest were born at term or within several days of term.*

GUNTHER *And none a fortnight early?*

WOLFF *I did not include any prematures.*

GUNTHER *I would like you to do that, because one would like to know whether this behaviour is coming with the date from conception or entirely from experience.*

WOLFF *I tried to get the age from conception more precisely, but it is very hard. Many mothers don't know for two months that they are pregnant and therefore don't have this information available. I have asked one obstetrician who has referred a number of cases to me, and in many cases he finds himself as stumped as I am.*

FOSS *You mentioned a gurgling noise made by the babies which you recorded and played to people who thought it was a laugh, but you said you thought it wasn't. On the other hand you are judging certain facial movements to be smiles, yet it is quite likely that if you took photographs and showed them to people, some would say they were not smiles. Why are you happy in the naming of one and not of the other? Is it because of the appearance of the thing, or do you guess at its function?*

WOLFF *Both. It looks like a smile and it has the effect on the mother of being a smile.*

THOMAS *Do you think that the organic state going along with smiling is the same in a baby of one month as it is in a child of 18 months?*

WOLFF *I don't think one can make inferences about the organic or emotional states. What I want to say is the morphological mechanism is there, and that the smile is not a contortion due to gas pains. But* one can add that the smile is incompatible with a disturbed or distressed state.

AMBROSE *If a stimulus is too intense, it will result in a distressed state, and if it is too weak it will not even claim attention.*

WOLFF *Certainly stimuli must be within these limits to elicit smiling, and these limits vary with the baby's state of alertness.*

BOWLBY *This pat-a-cake game is a curious kind of stimulus. Are there any other rhythmical movements which you have tried?*

WOLFF *In some babies after about four weeks, I get a smile if I bounce them on their legs. But some rhythms put them to sleep. Rocking can be effective, and so can rapid tapping of the spinal cord, at about two taps a second.*

AINSWORTH *Could you say more about the stimuli you have used to elicit following with the eyes?*

WOLFF *Because of my interest in Piaget I have been comparing the attention-getting value of the human face and other objects of the same size, and I find that up to two months the crucial factor is movement.*

AMBROSE *But you said that habituation to the human face was slower than to masks and things.*

WOLFF *That may be because part of the face, the eyes, are constantly moving anyway. My impression is that movement is more important than contour at this age.*

GUNTHER *It's often said that when a baby is being breast-fed it stares at the mother's face, even from the first day.*

WOLFF *I've tried taking by stop-watch the time spent on the mother's face, and looking into space, and looking into space wins easily for bottle-fed babies. With breast-fed babies it depends to some extent how the baby is held.*

The Natural History of a Family

PETER H. WOLFF

A. Introduction

In my work on the development of affect expressions I have spent many hours a week for several months at a time in the homes of healthy middle-class families, and I have had the opportunity to follow how newborn infants are introduced and integrated into the atmosphere of the family's daily life.

When several participants at this conference referred to the 'attachment behaviour' of human infants and sought to identify the specific mechanisms by which the child is 'attached' to its mother, I thought it might be useful if I were to present my impressions of one such family atmosphere during a baby's first three months when feeding and giving, getting fed and getting, were the crucial issues between mother and child; and to show how the infant's *Umwelt* may already contribute to his development shortly after birth. In my observations I have been impressed by the infinite variety of avenues through which mother and child may reach out to each other to establish a delicate balance of mutual regulation; and by the great variety of uses to which the baby's inborn apparatuses can be put so that his development may be moulded to fit in with the cultural and personal traditions of the caretaking parents. I therefore became interested to discover what were the constraints placed on the mother which would determine the way in which she would establish a relationship of mutuality with her child.

It seems to me important not only to describe the phenomenal world of the families I was studying and thereby perhaps to increase our knowledge of how healthy families live in spite of our textbooks, but also to emphasize how complex, individual, and at times apparently conflict-ridden, were the social forces of human mothering which in the lower animal species are guaranteed by relatively rigid, stereotypic stimulus-response chains. After having observed families from varied cultural backgrounds, I could not believe that genetic factors and biological demands were the primary constraints which dictated to a mother how she was to care for her baby, although such biological determinants might limit the range of her choices.

To organize my observations I adopted a technique of configurational description that Erikson had used successfully to study the psychosocial life of American Indian tribes (Erikson, 1950, pp. 95–160). I did not attempt to interpret the manifest behaviour by dynamic rules of transformation in order to uncover the underlying motives and defences and in order to explain the contradictions in overt behaviour. Instead I took the phenomena at their face value and assumed that despite possible underlying conflicts, these phenomena might in their overt form also have an adaptive significance. Finally, I tried to discover the binding social forces among the various items of behaviour that gave the family atmosphere the appearance of coherent unity and psychosocial health.

B. The family

The 'K' family are lower-middle-class Boston Irish Catholics. The 'Irish Catholics' of Boston constitute a distinct sociological group who since their arrival in New England have maintained a strong group identity, cemented by specific traditions and an historically determined socio-economic status (Handlin, 1959).

The potato famines in Southern Ireland at the middle and end of the nineteenth century came at a time when the Irish peasantry had been impoverished and exploited for decades by its British landlords. Hundreds of thousands of emigrants spent their last savings for passage to America; they came without the money to take them from the overcrowded harbour cities in the east into sections of the country where other immigrants had found adequate employment. The Irish immigrants were rooted to their debarkation point, crowded into slum sections of the larger cities, and forced to take any employment offered. Like the Irish peasants, the 'good families' of Boston, after coming from England, had maintained their identity as aristocratic Protestants, and they were again in a position to exploit the Irish – no longer as potato farmers, but as servants, maids, casual day labourers, and underpaid factory workers. The very condition of exploitation from which the Irish had thought to escape by emigrating faced them again. A newly formed *Lumpenproletariat*, deprived of its identity as a peasant class, sought for group solidarity in aggressive fraternal organizations, Benevolent Societies, and Catholic lay orders. The old suspicion, belligerence, and organized antagonism between Irish and English in America have persisted into the present, despite the gradual improvement of the Irishman's lot and his political ascendancy over the conservative Protestant factions of New England society. Perhaps this historical development played a significant role in the K family's orientation towards non-Irish authority, institutions, and moral values.

The father, Mr K, was 35 and 36 during the two successive years of observation; he was an only child of parents who married late in life. He is employed by a gas company where he started as a meter-reader and later became a white-collar worker; he holds a position of some authority, is competent in his work, and well liked by the employers.

The mother, aged 29 and 30, was a middle girl in a family of three sisters and three brothers. When I first met the family, Mr and Mrs K had had four children and one miscarriage in five years of marriage; the children were Joanne, 8, Jack, 7, Ronnie, 3, and Michael, who was my first 'subject' of intensive study. In the year following my first observation period another girl, Frances, was born, and also became a subject for my study.

The K's lived in a small, crowded apartment above a grocery store owned by Mrs K's mother and managed by her three brothers. Since I completed my observations, they have moved to their own house in the suburbs. Because Mr K was at work during most of my daily visits, my impressions were mainly about the mother's attitudes and ways of handling her children. Several times a week, however, when my schedule called for observations in the evening, I had the opportunity to observe the father with his wife and children. Mrs K's many anecdotes about her husband's life indicated that he was conscientious and took his family responsibilities seriously. He was easy-going, not strongly motivated to compete for economic advancement, and preferred to use his time for fishing, golf, and an occasional glass of beer. He did not think deeply about moral issues or questions of international politics, but was confident about what was right and wrong for himself and his family.

141

In contrast to this Mrs K showed a remarkable disrespect for and rebellion against all forms of institutionalized authority. For example, when the family doctor prescribed penicillin for one of the children and the illness improved spontaneously, Mrs K decided not to give the medicine, saved it in the medicine cabinet for another occasion, and herself prescribed the antibiotic for a minor illness for which the doctor had refused to give any medication.

Following her deliveries, Mrs K usually had a moderate anaemia for which the obstetrician prescribed supplementary iron. She refused to take iron because of its obnoxious taste, but faithfully reported to her obstetrician that she was taking her medicine, and regularly transferred pills from the bottle to the sink as a confirmation that she was following orders. Her disregard of medical advice was sufficiently circumspect so that she accepted the physician's advice whenever an illness was serious.

Mrs K had contempt for the wealthy medical specialists practising on Boston's finest street. Nevertheless she arranged to have herself and all the children treated by one of them at a reduced rate, mocked him to his face, and made fun of his patients. She had little faith in the germ theory of disease, and two weeks after the baby was born neither his milk nor his bottle was sterilized. The children were allowed to touch the baby, to feed, diaper, burp, and hold him, as long as they did not poke his eyes or stick their dirty fingers in his mouth. When one of the children had a cold, Mrs K half-heartedly attempted to isolate the infected child from the baby, but gave up because the crowded conditions made effective isolation impossible. Her apparent disregard for rules of hygiene was tempered by common sense; the baby was always clean and physically well cared for.

With great delight Mrs K often told me how she exploited the local tradespeople. The druggist was black-mailed into free cups of coffee and candy for the children because the K family 'after all, did the largest volume of business in the neighbourhood', while the butcher was pressured into giving extra portions of meat. Mrs K's outright demands, presented in a teasing fashion, left the shopkeepers speechless and impotent to deal with her aggressive frankness. Policemen, although as tough in Boston as in other cities, were incapable of fining or even warning Mrs K for minor traffic violations; her outrageous excuses and obvious lies invariably got her off with a wink and a friendly smile.

When one of her children was placed in a parochial hospital for minor surgery, Mrs K had the situation well in hand by the third day. For her, nuns had been a source of irritation and an object for defiance since her own parochial-school days. Now, as the mother of a sick child, she openly defied the authority of the nuns. She visited the hospital when it suited her and overruled the objections of the administration by asking how anyone could expect her to take care of four children at home and at the same time visit her daughter in the hospital at arbitrary visiting hours. She berated the nurses for their lack of attention to all of the children in the hospital, brought her daughter extra rations because she thought the hospital diet was inadequate, and forced through a special privilege of milk with each meal for her daughter.

From this and many similar examples, one may gain the impression that Mrs K was an egocentric bully who butted her way through regulations and pushed the letter of the law to its limits. This was by no means the case. She had a strong sense of justice, and when she respected the source of authority, she conformed without hesitation. In most of her daily affairs she seemed to be guided by a personal code of right and wrong to which she adhered with only minor infractions.

Signs of sexual precocity in her children, and particularly the dawning awareness of sexuality in Joanne, caused her great anxiety. She was enraged when Joanne reported that she had played 'house' in a basement with several boys, and threatened to break Joanne's arm if this behaviour should ever recur. She was also ambivalent about her own sexuality; she relished telling dirty jokes which she had heard from her girl friends, but by the obstetrician's report was profoundly ignorant and quite phobic about concrete sexual matters. The prohibitive teachings of her church probably reinforced her own anxieties and hysterical avoidance; but matters of sex, pregnancy, childbirth, and the permission to enjoy sexual relations, were the one clearly defined aspect of Mrs K's life where she showed major conflict.

The prospect of endless pregnancies was a horror to her, as it is to many of the women in this subculture, who look forward to a long succession of pregnancies from which they can anticipate release only at the time of the menopause. During the first trimester of her last three pregnancies Mrs K had become depressed and, according to her own report, somewhat disoriented. Yet she often joked with

143

me that nuns should have four or five children of their own, then they wouldn't be so righteous and superior. In jest she wanted to write a letter to the Pope complaining about the birth control laws and requesting a Papal dispensation.

The relation between the parents was not easily formulated in clinical terms, since I had no special knowledge about their inner life and was limited to describing their observable encounters. I was impressed that a genuine feeling of friendship which underlay their transactions, a mutual respect and understanding, an agreement on most important issues and the agreement to disagree on others, were all hidden below a surface of casual teasing, mutual demeaning, horseplay and wrestling; any open show of tenderness was rare.

Mrs K was clearly in charge of the house management, although she left the major decisions to her husband. Mr K was quite capable of making up his mind, but took his wife's wishes into consideration. The plan to move to a new house came from Mrs K, because she wanted her children to have a safer place to play. Mr K was content to remain where they lived, but when he found a promising house they looked at it together, and in the end Mrs K's word decided which house they would buy.

A month after returning home from the lying-in hospital Mrs K was exhausted and depressed by her housework; she simply 'took off' to spend three days with her mother and left the family in her husband's hands. On her return, Mr K jeered at her for being soft, they had a brief exchange of joking taunts, and Mrs K resumed her duties with vigour and good spirits. She enjoyed accusing her husband of being lazy, soft, and of having it much too good because he could sit down all day to gossip with his friends while she had to work her fingers to the bone. Mr K always had the ready answer that while he slaved away to earn their keep, she sat drinking tea, looking at television, and playing with the children. In private Mr K often told me how hard it was for his wife to have all this work on her hands and to care for the children at the same time. He was sensitive to moments when she was overworked and irritated, and then made a real effort to help out at home. In her turn, Mrs K confided to me that her husband was conscientious, that he was really a model husband and never wasted any money; he didn't take off time for his own pleasure, and took pride in raising his family. I had the impression that she appreciated him deeply.

Whenever the father took over the care of the baby after the mother had defiantly thrust Michael at him with the statement, 'Here – he's your son; take care of him – I'm busy and he likes you better anyway,' she hovered over his shoulder, snorted and made derisive guffaws about his clumsiness. In the end she always took her son back, saying, 'Come on, let me show you how a real mother does it. Michael obviously prefers his mother. I know how to do it – you men don't.'

But when Mr K thought that she was handling the baby too roughly, she gave him a long, searching glance and accusingly told him that thanks to him, she had had some previous experience in raising babies and that she knew what she was doing. Such exchanges certainly had a sting of aggression, but they seemed innocuous in the total context of jovial teasing.

The parents rarely went out together, although Mr K sometimes packed his wife off to a restaurant when she had enough of housework and craved some exotic food. Television was their major occupation in the evening; they never went to the movies, and read only newspapers. When friends came, the visits were casual, perhaps for a glass of beer and some gossip after dinner. I never observed an occasion when they attended any formal social function together. Each parent had one night out a week, and Mrs K attended her card parties, where she ostensibly played cards, but spent most of the time telling off-colour jokes with the other women and deriding men for their heartlessness. Mr K rarely made use of his evenings out to have a beer with his old Army cronies. Usually he was content to stay at home, to play with the children, and to make acid criticisms about the corruption of the local (Irish) politicians.

The parents treated their children with respect, but with that respect for children which assumes that in the end grown-ups know what is best. There was little evidence of the 'child's tyranny over his parents' about which so much is written in sociological studies of the American family. The three oldest children had one room together in which they did what they wanted. Each of them had his own specific daily assignments to do. Ronnie, who had never been assigned to any chores before because she was the youngest, assumed Jack's duties when the new baby came home; Jack took on Joanne's former jobs, and Joanne was now entrusted with the purchase of groceries and other financial transactions. It was simply assumed that the work would be done, and the children didn't question this assumption. They fought freely among themselves for their rights, and the mother generally encouraged them to settle their own disputes without running to her. But when the circus got out of hand, either mother or father intervened to protect the loser. Because Ronnie had been a month premature at birth and had always remained small in stature, she was the family pet, but she refused to exploit this position to advance her own cause. Instead she became a fierce fighter, challenged anyone who teased her beyond her point of tolerance, and defiantly balled her fists to lay low whoever overstepped his limits. When she could not maintain a brave front and broke into tears, Mrs K (who had encouraged Ronnie to be tough and defiant) came to the rescue and comforted her by inventing games in which they revenged themselves on the boys or men who had teased Ronnie. Ronnie's touching sessions with her mother lasted for as long as they both were amused, even when a large backlog of work pressed on Mrs K. With Joanne the mother was equally comforting, although in ways more appropriate to the older girl's needs, but when Jack found the rough-housing with his father or with his siblings too tough and ran to her, she was contemptuous. She tried to shame him into fighting back, but if he broke into tears she weakened and allowed him to sit on her lap. Mr K, who loved to rough-house with his children, was also disgusted when Jack acted like a coward. A father's outraged objection to his oldest son's signs of cowardice, and the son's tendency to passive avoidance, was a pattern that I had observed before in several Irish Catholic families and about which I have heard from other parents in consultations.

Without doubt, Mrs K was highly competitive with the men in her family, and deeply resented the 'double standard'. When her father-in-law offered to give Jack $5.00 for his excellent marks in school but gave Joanne only $2.00 because her marks weren't as good, Mrs K raised the roof and forbade her father-in-law to give away any money unless it was equally distributed. She resented the fact that the priests invariably favoured the men during confession and blamed the women for all sins when demanding penance. She conveyed her feminist beliefs to her daughters by encouraging them to fight for their rights, telling them that this was a hard world in which women had to see to it that men didn't step on them; and despite her phobic attitude to sex, by playfully encouraging Ronnie and

Joanne to tease, cajole, and blackmail men for special privileges and gifts.

The parents shared the responsibility of discipline; Mrs K was incapable of striking her children, and when her words did not have the desired effect she threatened the children with physical punishment that would be administered by the father as soon as he came home. Mr K rarely struck his children, but then without hesitation. Never during the six months of observation did I see either parent in a state of uncontrolled or nearly uncontrolled rage with the children. To be sure, they showed their annoyance and anger quickly and openly, but then got over it just as quickly and re-established friendly relations with a minimum residual of gnawing hostility.

When one of the children disobeyed Mrs K, she threatened to send one or all of them to the poorhouse. To do so, she used a phrase which was so familiar to the children that they recited it with the mother. The chorus of five voices reciting Mrs K's threat in unison made her unable to remain serious; she burst into laughter, raised her open hand as if to strike them, and then sent them scurrying back to their own affairs. At other times she threatened to have them put into jail or hospital, where the doctor would remove various organs. A pingpong paddle always hung in sight in the kitchen as a symbolic and concrete reminder of corporal punishment. Although the paddle was vigorously used on occasions, the children referred to it with great glee and as a joke hid it so their mother couldn't find it. Ronnie often invoked its use as a way to keep her older siblings in line.

Certain misbehaviours were punished severely, swiftly, and without hesitation. When Ronnie began to bite neighbourhood children, Mrs K took her aside and bit her in the arm so hard that she drew blood. Ronnie never bit again. When Jack began to spit at other boys, Mrs K reported this to her husband, who took a mouthful of tea and spat it at Jack's face. After that Jack never spat again.

During my second year of observation, when Michael had discovered the gas stove and defied Mrs K's prohibitions against turning it on, she finally took his hand and held it so close to the fire that he was hurt but not burned. Michael was obviously distressed by this punishment, and Mrs K comforted him in her arms, cooed softly to him, but never apologized either to him or to me for her harsh action. For several weeks Michael stopped playing with the stove,

147

but then had to be reminded once more in the same way before he permanently abandoned playing with fire.

From simply listening to their voices in the house or on the street, Mrs K had an uncanny intuition where her children were, what they were doing, how imminent a fight was. Even while busy with the laundry, washing the dishes, or playing with Michael, she had her ears tuned to the noises on the street, and if these suggested that a dangerous situation might arise, she was at the window regulating the dispute from the second floor before I had heard a thing. Her alertness and anticipatory anxiety were partly justified by frequent accidents in which neighbourhood children were struck by passing automobiles. The one rule which Mrs K impressed on her children over and over with various bloody threats was a prohibition against crossing the street at dangerous intersections.

In minor matters of discipline Mrs K was consistently inconsistent. No matter how she had resolved to handle a minor crisis or to settle some issue of discipline beforehand, she changed her mind at least once. When she had forbidden her children to eat sweets before a meal or had limited their time of television watching, a sad face or a lot of unhappiness quickly changed her mind and she gave in. After she had decided that Joanne should stay home because of a recent bout of the measles, she eventually sent the girl out to play in the street, although Joanne was still on quarantine. Long after Ronnie had recovered from a pout because she had not been allowed to go out, Mrs K capriciously decided Ronnie needed fresh air and sent her out to play, much against Ronnie's loud protests. However, when she had made a decision which she considered important for the children's welfare, she was inflexible in her resolve.

Mrs K's attitude towards food, and the atmosphere which she created around issues of feeding and getting fed, proved to be important not only in her interchange with the other children but also with Michael as soon as he was born. Neither the parents nor the children were obese, and although Mrs K loved to nibble at some food or drink all day, she was sufficiently underweight so that she had wangled a semi-permanent dispensation from the local priest to eat meat on Fridays. The significance of food as a social medium had nothing to do with the quality of food or the quantity which the children were either forced or allowed to eat. Their diet was decidedly boring. Occasionally Mrs K haphazardly insisted that Joanne should

148

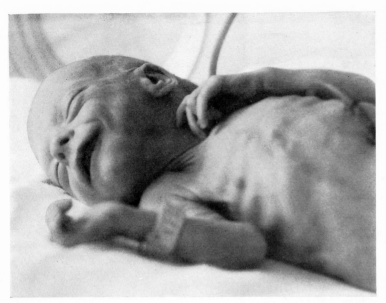

PLATE 18. 28-week gestation – premature with intestinal atresia; 3 days after surgery, 6 days post partum, 2 weeks ante mortem

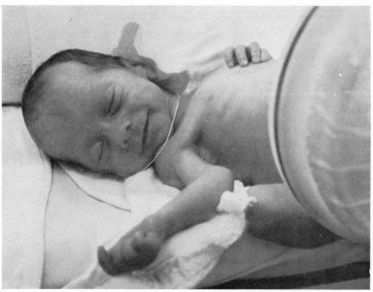

PLATE 19. 30-week gestation – normal premature 'asleep'

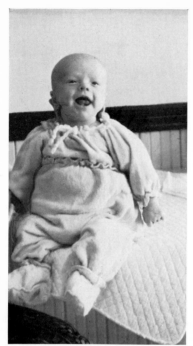

PLATE 20. The social smile, seen from the third week onwards

PLATE 21. 4th week – alert-inactive after meal; eye to eye contact

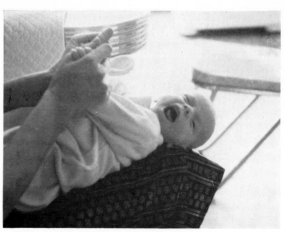

PLATE 22. Pat-a-cake played by mother elicits chortling 'laughter' in 5-week infant

try to eat a balanced diet instead of drinking her daily quart of milk, but since the girl flourished and showed no signs of wasting away, she was not coerced to eat more than she wanted. The children were allowed to eat as much or as little as they pleased, but they had to eat what was prepared or else go without. Mrs K was always pleased to prepare a simple lunch for me when I observed during the middle of the day, but she never pressed the issue when I refused a meal. I was also invited to join the family at supper if I was observing during that time, but when I did accept, no effort was made to prepare anything out of the ordinary for me. Between meals the children always had some candy, ice-cream, or other sweets; the candy they got from home was limited, but the children knew how to extract a few pennies from relatives, or neighbourhood shopkeepers, by running useless errands. In mock outrage, Mrs K was always pleased to hear that Ronnie or Joanne had blackmailed a storekeeper to give her a few cents for bringing him a cup of coffee that he didn't want. In the summertime the icebox held a large pot of ice-cream, a fountain scoop, and an ice-cream-cone dispenser. When a K child came home after school to change his clothes, he was accompanied by a troop of neighbourhood children who all in their turn received an ice-cream cone. One or another neighbour child often stayed to eat supper or lunch, and either Jack or Joanne was often away to eat with one of his or her friends. The paternal grandfather, whose wife was chronically ill in a nursing home, usually took his supper with the family. When he complained about the lack of variety in the diet, in a mocking way, he was bludgeoned into supplying expensive cuts of meat or other delicacies. Mrs K's brothers, who managed the grocery store and came in the afternoons to share lunch, a cup of tea, or a glass of beer, also made their contributions to the family's grocery supply. Since I had stipulated at the beginning a stipend for each month of observation, no contribution to the food supply was expected of me; but when I occasionally brought candy or small toys for the children on a holiday, these were accepted freely, without embarrassment, and as if it were in the normal course of things that I should bring something.

This was the general picture of the family at the time when Michael was born and I began my observations. Much of what I have reported so far was actually recorded after the boy was born, since I had made only a few visits to the K family before Michael's birth.

When Mrs K began to have regular contractions on the expected date of delivery, she came into the hospital, while her husband notified me. When I met her in the labour room (Mr K had remained at home to stay with the children), she confessed that she had drunk a milkshake shortly before coming in, out of fear that she would not get enough to eat in the hospital. She knew perfectly well that her indiscretion would preclude gas anaesthesia and require her to have a spinal anesthetic that she hated and feared. After a short second stage of labour during which she swore like a trooper, condemned her mother, and particularly the physician in the labour room, she gave birth to a healthy eight-pound boy, Michael, who cried spontaneously with great vigour. Mrs K's first response, immediately after the delivery, was to ask for a corned-beef sandwich. Then she asked about the boy, his sex and his weight. After inspecting him, grunting with pleasure, commenting with mock disgust that it was just like a boy to come so quickly, and complaining that he had all her husband's features and none of hers, she again asked for a corned-beef sandwich. Three more times during the remaining hour in the recovery room she asked for food.

On the following day she admitted that the baby was cute and well shaped, but seemed more concerned to find out about her bad behaviour and histrionics in the labour room the night before. She knew she had blasphemed, but wanted to know precisely what she had said. When I told her that the doctors had gotten the worst of her attack, she was amused, although she pretended to be ashamed.

By neurological and physical examination the baby was healthy, but on the second day after birth I began to worry because he had a projectile emesis after at least two of his feedings every day. The house officers were not concerned with the vomiting, since the baby retained his other feedings and regained his birth weight within the expected time; Mrs K blandly took it for granted that the vomiting was further evidence that Michael was a typical 'K baby', since all her other children had done the same thing as babies.

Mrs K elected to bottle-feed Michael, as she had done with her previous children; and according to hospital routine the baby was brought to her four times a day. She fed him quickly, disregarded the vomiting, took him back to the nursery long before any of the other mothers had finished their feedings, and teased the nurses that they could feed him again if he got too noisy. She didn't want to bother with him because the hospitalization was her annual rest period to which she had looked forward; and naïve as I was, I considered this a rather ominous sign of maternal rejection. She preferred to socialize on the maternity floor or to watch television, and generally indulged in passive pleasures. By malingering and joking she adroitly avoided the household duties and religious observations required of all mothers in this Catholic hospital; but by the fourth day she had tired of the hospital routine, was restless, missed her children, and was anxious to go home to help out her husband. She also resented the hospital because she could not have her cup of tea whenever she wanted it, and successfully prevailed upon the obstetrician to let her out before her scheduled departure. When she and Michael returned home she quickly settled down to her practised routine, took on the new child and all other household duties with good spirits. No outside helpers came in to assist her, and she snorted with contempt about women who cannot manage a household and children on their own. She scorned the help offered by the public health nurses because she considered them to be nosy busybodies with less knowledge about child care than she had, and so invented many excuses to prevent the nurses from coming. Several times she effectively put them off with statements that it wouldn't be practical since her baby psychiatrist was there and could not be disturbed. Despite her fatigue and some early signs of 'post-partum blues', she resumed the full schedule of her household duties but let her husband know in roundabout ways about her heavy work load. Despite the added work load she found time during the early weeks to gossip endlessly with me in friendly fashion. Usually she arranged this by keeping Michael on the kitchen table, where he slept, ate, and was diapered, and where I observed him. Mrs K claimed she wanted to have him around where she could watch him and where he could keep her company. The baby's persistent vomiting began to trouble her enough so that she called the pediatrician several times and experimented in various ways to keep the feedings under control. Nevertheless she quickly resorted to the 'propping' method of feeding him (Plate 23*a*, *b*), and claimed that this was necessary because she was so busy with other work. During the entire time while the baby was fed by propping, and could see his mother with relative ease, she sat with me at the kitchen table, talking, smoking, and drinking her cup of tea. After the child had

151

finished the bottle she began to play with him, holding him in her lap, cuddling and talking with him in an absorbed fashion. There was almost no body contact between them during feedings (before Michael received solid food), but the total time of bodily contact after feeding and at odd times during the day was as long as or longer than the contact between other mothers and children I have observed who breast-fed or bottle-fed in a more orthodox fashion. Specialists on the mother-child interaction who attribute great significance to body contact between mother and child during the feeding period might reconsider how important the contiguity of contact and getting fed is for establishing an adequate 'attachment', especially when the opportunity for visual contact is ample.

Mrs K sensed exactly when Michael was 'ready to play', and never seemed to force the child into a relation with her at times when his attention was absorbed by something else.

Her consistent inconsistency showed itself when she supposedly wanted to initiate a stable four-hour feeding cycle in Michael. Every effort at firmness inevitably failed within two days because she gave in when she thought that Michael was suffering from hunger pains, even though her verbal responses suggested that she considered the baby's cry an intrusion on her routine. Her claim that she would have preferred to keep him sleeping and quiet for the whole day was contradicted by the way in which she rocked him to sleep after a meal, which seemed to be blatantly calculated to keep him awake. In the same way, she spoke gently and soothingly to him in a manner almost calculated to put him back to sleep, when she ostensibly wanted to awaken him to give him his scheduled feeding. Before Michael's arrival she had resolved not to spoil him; she was convinced that one spoils a baby by playing too much with him. Yet, as I have already indicated, she spent many hours playing with Michael and then laughed at herself in a defeated way, saying that she could not help herself, he was so much fun.

From Michael's second week at home she not only propped him but also fed him by the 'overflow method', which meant that she let the baby fill up on as much milk as he could take and burped him only at the end of the feeding. If and when he spit up, she judged this as a sign that he had had more than his fill and was simply spilling over the excess. It turned out to be a very satisfactory method of feeding; the baby thrived and gained weight steadily.

RHEINGOLD *You mean that this is how she judged how much the infant should take?*

That's right -- at least within some limits. Usually she gave a full bottle, first of four ounces, later five, and then six ounces. If the baby dozed off or if his sucking became dilatory, she tickled him or talked to him in order to start the sucking again; if the last ounce did not go in well she picked him up, rubbed him and held him to give him the last part of the bottle in the usual way. In the first week she had burped him after each ounce or ounce and a half, but later she just let him feed to completion and then burped him at the end. At two weeks she put Michael on a diet of warm cereal, and by three weeks he ate puréed fruits and vegetables, despite the fact that Mrs K had heard from various sources that newborn infants who eat solid foods may get cancer of the stomach. At three weeks Michael definitely preferred fruit to cereal, and Mrs K had to invent ways to trick him to eat his cereal. First he received one or two spoonfuls of fruit; when he expected a next spoonful of fruit he was surprised by a dose of cereal which Mrs K managed to get down him before he could object. At four weeks the baby was occasionally allowed to lick from an ice-cream cone, and by five weeks he occasionally got an afternoon treat of ice-cream.

By describing in detail Mrs K's first hours after delivery, I had meant to indicate how easy she found it to express her concrete, mundane wishes for food and comfort under circumstances when decorum and social expectation might have dictated other, loftier behaviour. Her preference for food over a wish to see her baby suggests a strong need for self-gratification after she herself had been depleted; no doubt Mrs K was ready to indulge herself with minor pleasures whenever the circumstances permitted it. I indicated that she usually smoked a cigarette and drank her cup of tea while Michael was getting his milk. She admitted that her use of various tricks to get the baby to sleep longer was to give her added peace and quiet. When she was worn out because Michael kept her awake at night, she went away for three days in order to get some sleep. When household duties pressed on her and spoiled her disposition, she amused herself by playing with the children.

However, when a child needed her attention she provided what was required without any awareness that she was making a sacrifice. On her return from the hospital Mrs K often craved for a milkshake, some chop suey, or other exotic food not available at home. When Ronnie was sent out to buy her the milkshake and returned not only with the milkshake but three friends and five fountain straws, the children had consumed the milkshake long before the mother had had a chance to taste of it. She looked at the empty carton, then at me, winked and laughed with a resigned shrug of the shoulder, and then scolded the children so that they ran out half amused and half frightened. After craving fresh shrimp for a whole week, Mrs K had prepared for herself a large dish of shrimp and then had gone out to run an errand. On her return she found that her husband had eaten the whole dish. She briefly roared at him, teased and boxed him, but when he was contrite and embarrassed, she laughed without further ado.

The only aspect of baby care where Mrs K's behaviour suggested any real conflict was the management and cleansing of the umbilical stump. She always kept it covered so as not to have to see it, and when it became mildly infected she begged me to apply the necessary ointment; several times she commented that she had had the same problem with her other children. Since she showed no such aversion to dirty diapers, faeces, urine, or vomitus, I inferred that her distress about the umbilical stump probably represented a covert sexual rather than an anal anxiety.

Since the dental bills were a large expense item in this family, both parents insisted that the children should brush their teeth religiously after every meal. Before retiring all the children had to wash themselves, and there was an occasional inspection of the ears and hands. Otherwise little emphasis was placed on cleanliness; bowel training had not been an issue with any of the children and was hardly ever mentioned in the family. When Ronnie had a brief spell of bed-wetting after Michael returned from the hospital, Mrs K simply shamed her into becoming dry by teasing her that only little girls wet their bed. For three days Ronnie could not behave like a baby, could not sit in her mother's lap or whimper or complain without hearing from her mother that this was the behaviour of a baby. Within that span of time Ronnie had stopped bed-wetting and the issue seemed settled. Like other children, the K children often returned home covered with dirt after playing in the streets or in the yard. As long as the soiled clothes were not for school wear or visits to

154

church, Mrs K accepted the inevitability of dirt, stripped and changed them into clean clothes, then dumped the dirty ones into the washing machine. Ronnie, whose mouth was usually smeared with chocolate, didn't like to be dirty and voluntarily brought her mother a wash-cloth at the end of the day to have her face wiped.

I have already mentioned that Mrs K spurned all regular help from a hired maid, from social welfare workers, and from her own rela-tions. Instead, however, one or two adolescent daughters of neigh-bourhood friends were usually with her in the afternoon or else available to help voluntarily with the baby and other household chores. Two of the girls especially had made Mrs K their confidante; they freely and seriously discussed their adolescent tribulations, and Mrs K took their problems about boy friends, nuns, and parents so seriously that I had the impression that she was vicariously reliving her own past. Their relation was more one between equals than between parent and daughters. Of interest in these friendships was the confidence with which the 14- or 16-year-old girls cared for the baby. They demonstrated the affectionate but unsentimental interest of a mature, well-practised mother who has gone through this many times before. Their certainty about what to do, and the cheerful pleasure with which they helped Mrs K without the expectation of payment, were in sharp contrast to their typically adolescent uncertainty about parents, boy friends, and growing up. They came not only to gossip with Mrs K, but to spend their free afternoons doing her household chores because they found the new baby irresistible. In handling Michael they were self-assured and matter-of-fact; they knew how to burp, diaper, and feed; they held and bathed the baby firmly and gently, and showed none of the helpless groping so characteristic of many primiparous mothers. When they discussed Michael and other babies with Mrs K, they spoke of their own coming parenthood and eventual large families as a matter of unfailing certainty, not as a source of embarrassment, anxiety, or romantic sentiment.

The picture I have drawn is far from complete; it has left out the personalities of the older children, neglected the father, and touched only briefly on Michael's development during the first three months after birth. He thrived during these months, smiled readily to voices and faces at the 'expected' times (see p. 119); by the end of the first month he slept through the night (six to seven hours), and in the daytime he spent long hours awake. Contrary to Mrs K's worries, he was not 'spoiled', but occupied himself by inspecting his hands, groping for toys, gurgling and talking to himself, without making demands on his mother. By five weeks he had established 'eye-to-eye contact' with Mrs K, and this greatly prolonged their play.

A year later when I was invited back to observe the new baby Frances, Michael was open and sociable, the apple of his parents' eye, and Ronnie's jealous possession. He stood and crawled, but did not yet walk with self-confidence. He could easily wheel his own baby-carriage back and forth, but preferred to support himself on the carriage by pushing it sideways when he experimented with walking. Although he tolerated the playful attacks of his brother and sisters, he struck back when he could get within their range. He had little difficulty letting his mother leave the room, and cheerfully accepted the substitute care of his sisters and the baby-sitters whenever the mother was away for any length of time.

C. The 'experiments'

Before summarizing my general impressions I would like to present two *ad hoc* experiments that highlight a characterological trait I had found in all the family members, and that I believe the mother had unconsciously instilled in her children by the way she attended to their everyday needs.

Ronnie at three and a half and four and a half years was my constant companion during the observation periods; she helped me to administer tests to Michael, made 'notes' and drew pictures while I recorded my observations. One day when I seriously asked her to give me some of her bottomless supply of candy, she surprised me by pulling all she had out of her pocket, dividing it in half, and then recommending to me which of the sweets tasted the best. I took a little of the candy to see if she was serious in her offer. She accepted my eating as a matter of course, and when I tried to return the remaining candy to her, she was adamant that it was for me. Afterwards and to my embarrassment in front of the amused mother, Ronnie often came to offer me a share of her candy. For example, she appeared one day with an all-day sucker of various colours, explained carefully that the different colours represented different flavours, and insisted that I must taste from all of the regions. The older K children at first thought I was teasing them when I repeated the game of asking for some of their candy, and were less ready to part with their possessions. But when they discovered that I was serious, they surrendered some of their candy, and on later occasions voluntarily came to share with me. For these children candy was by no means an article of no value; whenever one of the children had some in his hand and the others did not, there was a row until Mrs K had made some equitable arrangement for the deprived child.

In the second experiment I systematically repeated with Michael what I had observed anecdotally in Ronnie. During the second year of observation, when Michael was 13 or 14 months old, he often sat in his high chair and stuffed himself with his favourite dry cereal. When I came to him and held out my hand to indicate that I wanted some of what he was eating, he immediately understood what I wanted, laughed, put a piece of cereal in my hand, and watched while I ate, before he returned to his observation of the street scene. When I intruded on his play again and offered my open mouth, he understood the gesture, placed some food in my mouth, and laughed hilariously when I ate it. We then varied the game; when I put food in his mouth, he ate it, when I put it into his hand, he put it into his mouth. At other times I offered my own mouth after having put food into his hand; usually he fed me but sometimes himself. In the most complex variation of this game – when, after he had placed food in my mouth, I offered to him what I had in my teeth – he became confused about whether he was to eat the cereal or give it back to me. Otherwise Michael showed no doubt about the intention of the game, no hesitation about giving me his food, and no reluctance to accept what I offered him. On subsequent days the same games yielded the same results.

Since then I have tried the experiment on other children of the same age who were raised in different, and equally adequate, homes. Never have I found the same degree of freedom to give and take as I have seen in Michael. Some children reluctantly entered into the game, made a half-smiling, half-crying face when I actually ate what they had painfully offered me. Once they had learned their lesson they rejected the game and never again offered me anything. Other children never made the initial gesture to give me anything.

D. Summary

My purpose in bringing these anecdotes and '*ad hoc*' experiments (which have become a part of my routine testing procedure) was to show some possible influences of the family's personal and cultural traditions and the ways in which Michael and Ronnie had adapted to their social environment.

I assumed that a common thread which reappeared throughout the wide range of Mrs K's apparently unrelated and idiosyncratic styles of behaviour contributed to the ease with which Ronnie and Michael willingly shared their food with me, allowed themselves to be given to, and at the same time 'got to give to' others. As soon as Michael came home from the hospital he was exposed to an apparently careless, casual feeding pattern in which the mother indulged herself as readily as him. She felt free enough from inner constraint and from social expectations so that she supplied herself whenever the occasion arose. The concept of 'the devoted mother', of which she was justifiably suspicious on various counts, did not dictate to her how to raise Michael. Perhaps it was this freedom to give to herself when she felt depleted which made her equally ready to give her food, her time, and her affection freely to her children when they required 'sacrifices' from her.

She could withstand authoritative psychological prejudices about 'good feeding' techniques and child-rearing practices because she 'knew' from her own apprenticeship how things ought to be done. What she had learned in her apprenticeship, as a baby-sitter to her own younger siblings and perhaps as an adolescent baby-sitter to neighbourhood children, was embedded in a tradition of rebellion against an Anglo-Saxon Protestant Ethic. I am assuming that the historically determined and culturally perpetuated antagonisms to non-Irish institutions may have freed Mrs K to throw off moral values alien to her, and may have nurtured a rebellion against the vested cultural, moral, and economic interests, as well as the exploitation of shopkeepers and policemen.

Perhaps because of this, both father and mother found it easier to express their annoyance and anger at each other and the children without a crippling sense of guilt, since openly expressed anger was part of their cultural currency. Every storm blew up and then over quickly; the children had no doubt that they could be punished, but had also no doubt that after the score was settled and the debt was paid, nothing more would come and they could expect their mother to take them back into her lap.

I am not proposing that propping the bottle is the *sine qua non* of good mothering; nor that only a consistent inconsistency in parental regulations will steer children safely between compulsive adherence to existing laws and anarchic chaos; nor that every disturbing anti-social act against peers must be punished swiftly by the law of the talion.

Any of the 'techniques' I described, if taken out of its context and transplanted into a culture with different traditions, different balances, and different hopes for the children's future, might have unfortunate results or would be submerged as insignificant in the overall impact of family rearing patterns. Thus the patterns I described were neither health-promoting nor pathogenic in themselves.

I am suggesting, however, that in this family and others like it, whose economic history dictated that the sons would one day become day-labourers, priests, politicians, and bar-keeps, the daughters would one day become mothers of large families – these 'techniques' had been essential in the total configuration. In the face of a general disruption of the American family structure, and despite the greater range of opportunities now available to the Boston Irish Catholics, these techniques have retained their internal logic to the extent that Boston Irish families maintain themselves as relatively integral and autonomous from the 'great levelling process'. To study the logic of mutuality regulations such as those I have described may therefore be useful to remind us how relative is the significance of any one stereotype behaviour in the establishment of 'attachment behaviour'. Each attachment behaviour itself may be a universal phenomenon, and its origin may be biologically determined; but the adaptive uses to which such congenital apparatuses are put in the social context go far beyond the phylogeny of the human species.

Although Mrs K fed Michael and fulfilled his biological requirements in an adequate fashion, she rarely held him during a feeding. There was none of the intimacy between mother and child around this first vital transaction which we have justifiably assumed to be of primary importance in the attachment of infant to parent and of parent to offspring. Instead of cuddling him and providing tactile nutriment together with milk and with the opportunity to suck, Mrs

K treated herself to tea and cigarettes while Michael ate. Yet, or perhaps because of such self-indulgences, she found ample opportunity to engage with him in many hours of body contact, and to play when Michael was ready to play. By giving with equal ease to herself and to her children, she may have instilled in Michael the balance between an expectation to be given when the need arose, and a dawning awareness that he who gets freely from others can also give with the certainty that he will not thereby be depleted or diminished. The easy give-and-take with his mother may have created in Michael (as in the other children) the unformulated expectation that with generosity comes the privilege of making forthright demands without that burden of guilt which so often inhibits us from accepting what others have to offer.

Discussion following Dr Wolff's second paper

WOLFF *Perhaps I should explain that this description of family relationships is a bonus that comes with my specific studies of the baby and its mother; but I have come to believe that the isolated study of particular items of behaviour out of their context leads to all kinds of false conclusions.*

BOWLBY *You are really following the ethologists and studying the animal in its natural habitat.*

WOLFF *What is striking, and what I had not expected, was that one could obtain so much information by simply observing and chatting, without questioning or testing the parents in any formal, systematic way . . . they volunteer an amazing amount.*

AINSWORTH *You do not interview?*

WOLFF *I have avoided asking any directed questions except on small and apparently innocuous points.*

SCHAFFER *In the synopsis which you circulated for your original paper, I remember there was a reference to your interest in trying to conceptualize the material in Piaget terms. Is this the material you will use?*

WOLFF *No. Although I think Piaget's structural concept of schema is useful here, I have not really tried to put the observed behaviour in terms of schemata, assimilation, and accommodation. Possibly the schema is applicable as the psychological structure for conceptualiz-*

160

ing social as well as intellectual adaptation; and I believe one could go beyond the description of formal social interaction which Piaget considered in his book The Moral Judgement of the Child. *It doesn't seem to me to be a large theoretical step to go from a sensorimotor schema to Erikson's (1950) concept of mode and modality; their functional properties and structural derivation have much in common.*

GEWIRTZ *You have reported that the Boston babies of Irish descent appear precocious in some of their behaviours relative to other babies you have studied. How do you explain this phenomenon in terms of your conception of the ways in which the environment could have impact on the child?*

WOLFF *Well, if we consider the K baby, he spent a good part of the day on the kitchen table, and there were always other children and adults around. Although I really cannot specify the mechanisms of inter- action that should make this possible, it seemed quite likely that a lot of social stimulation might have made the baby respond earlier by smiling and cooing to social stimuli. I think this would be the kind of correlation that you're implying. But I don't think it is specific to social interchanges; Michael's hand-eye, hand-ear and hand-hand co-ordination, and the extent of his visual explorations, also seemed precocious as compared to other children I have observed, although I don't think we have any normative data on this material, and Piaget's three cases will have to serve for the present. For example, when I gave two rattles to Michael at eight weeks, one containing beads and one empty, he always shook that hand which held the rattle with the beads more than the other one, even when I exchanged the rattles. Now I don't have sufficient data to make more than a guess that this child was precocious in rattle-shaking as well as in smiling; he acted as if he not only wanted to shake but also wanted to make the sound recur. If this speculation is correct, it would correspond to a transi- tional phase going towards Piaget's third stage of sensorimotor development (four to eight months). Obviously Michael could only 'want' to shake the rattle with the beads in it after he had been given a rattle with beads to shake. If we accept Piaget's motivation concept of functional need, it was the exposure to the novelty which created Michael's need to repeat; and the more novelties to which the child is exposed, the greater will be the range of different actions he 'needs to repeat' in order to adapt to the novelties he has encountered. There- fore a richer environment or a heightened degree of experience should within limits lead to an acceleration of development. Probably, however, you cannot push this acceleration far, since there is also an inherent maturational timetable of the kind Erikson has spoken about, and a tendency towards* equilibration *about which Piaget speaks. This tendency towards equilibration implies to me that there has to be a steady progression of newly acquired adaptations all across the board, and you cannot push any one behaviour pattern out of proportion to all others and still get an orderly sequence of development.*

A colleague of mine, Dr Burton White, is now engaged in experiments with socially deprived babies in a foundling home to see how fast and how far one can accelerate certain developmental sequences, by a varying degree of articulation in the environment and by increasing the opportunities for apprenticing certain sensorimotor functions.

GEWIRTZ *In your first paper, the question arose about how you would interpret these relationships. For instance, which stages does the child go through so that he would come to play more with the rattle, or so that he would be precocious in some of his perceptual responses? How would you explain the correlations you were just describing with your model?*

WOLFF *I really think this would raise issues about which I don't want to take a theoretical position at this point.*

GEWIRTZ *I find I can't imagine what sort of theoretical position you would take.*

BOWLBY *I think, Jack, that it is difficult for you to imagine that most of us are in a very muddled state about theory. I think there is a difference between those who have a very precise theory with very precise expectations and who then try to make sense of data, and those of us – and I speak as one – who are interested in certain observations because they seem to be relevant to matters of consequence such as mental health, and then later struggle to discover some sort of theory which begins to make sense of them. I don't know Peter's condition, but it wouldn't surprise me if he was still struggling to clarify what sorts of theory are relevant.*

WOLFF *I will put my neck in a noose if you want and speculate that those children who get a lot of stimulation early also acquire a greater variety of functional needs early – in other words, they seek contact with segments of the environment more actively. By exposure to more varieties of stimulation which the infant can assimilate, he begins to elaborate new schematic structures which in turn require repetitive action for stabilization – or in behavioural terms, newly discovered behaviours must be adapted.*

In a sense, therefore, Piaget's concept of motivation might be very useful. He assumes that there are no a priori *needs for practising action on object, but the contact with the object, which is controlled in part at least by the environment, creates a motivation specific to the novelty encountered as it is assimilated to an existing structure.*

SCHAFFER *Presumably there is an optimal amount of stimulation which each individual requires for his developmental progress. It is not a matter of providing as much as you possibly can – even if you simply bombard an infant in this way you will still not get him talking at the age of six months. One of the most intriguing things about all this is to find out what the optimum is for different infants.*

GEWIRTZ *Of course, that point should apply equally to any stimuli. That is, there should be an optimal level (along any of a number of dimensions, potentially) of the stimulus for producing, in the sense of eliciting, signalling, or reinforcing, any behaviour for which it is a relevant stimulus.*

WOLFF *I think we should add one more factor, namely the optimal time in the baby's daily life for presenting the stimulus object. For the study of attachment behaviour it seems to me very important to determine how well the mother can gauge her baby's readiness and willingness to respond in a particular way to a particular stimulus at a particular time.*

To return to your original question, it would seem that within limits, the more you do with a child at a favourable time, the more it will want to do with you.

GEWIRTZ *Do you conceive that there are original 'needs' involved here?*

WOLFF *Well, that is a different problem. I think we cannot overlook all the clinical evidence from which psychoanalysis has inferred instinctual drive motivation. I think even some of the ethologists are now coming full circle and speaking of central motivational states or superordinate drives which integrate discrete behaviour patterns. The evidence from many disciplines seems to indicate that a motivation concept like Piaget's 'need to function' cannot take care of all of human behaviour. What I was getting at before was that instinctual drives also cannot account for all motivations, and that for a certain range of adaptive behaviours which will develop into intellectual and perhaps social structures, a motivation concept such as the need to function may be very useful. With such a concept we may be able to reconcile the contradiction that on the one hand the child seems to develop according to an autochthonous timetable which is neither maturational in the embryological sense nor experiential in the learning theory sense; and on the other hand, the great deal of evidence that learning in its conventional sense obviously makes a difference and can speed up or slow down development. It seems to me quite possible, for example, that early in development every child requires a basic minimum amount of stimulation which is not of the same kind as instinctual drive gratifications. Without such minimal stimulation, the congenital adaptive structures will atrophy from disuse. Since those congenital structures are global, the newborn infant's stimulus hunger is syncretic and from the observer's point of view appears to be a nonspecific hunger for ubiquitous stimulation. But as the baby acquires psychological structures, and in accordance with these he articulates the environment more selectively, his stimulus hunger will also become more specific, and it will become a need for co-ordinated action on increasingly specific objects.*

GEWIRTZ *One of your last points may imply a notion not unlike one which Helson has termed 'adaptation level'; that is, where the level or rate of stimulation the organism has received, and hence comes to 'expect', might itself acquire the capacity to function as a stimulus for certain behaviours. This 'expectation' level perhaps may be best estimated as a central tendency of the range of the stimuli experienced previously by the organism, and would provide the context for its subsequent responses to the stimuli. This notion might predict an organism's approach, e.g. to food, in the sense that its hunger at any given time would depend on some average level of times passing between feeds, that is, on the rate at which food had been previously received (and responded to) and at which the organism had come to 'expect' it.*

WOLFF *Now wait a minute. I think there are some requirements that do not depend on experience. One of these is oxygen, another is food. The hunger a baby experiences does not depend on how much experience with eating he has had in the past.*

GEWIRTZ *But a level or rate of stimulation itself may acquire stimulus value for the organism, even to where it could acquire close control*

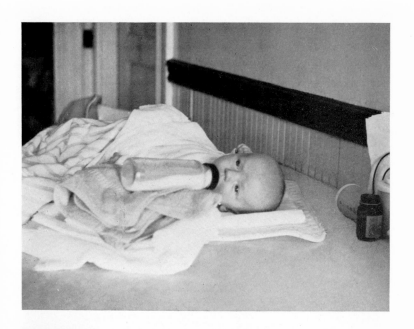

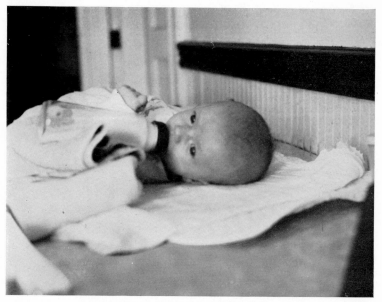

PLATE 23. Infant fed by method of propping

PLATE 24 Infant in the experimental situation.

over behaviours which would be related to basic organic requirements. He would, as it were, acquire an 'expectation' for the receipt of stimuli depending on the pattern of his receipt of stimuli in the past. The learning involved should occur particularly easily where the rate of stimulation is regular (periodic) rather than intermittent; and aspects of these patterns could for the organism acquire the capacity to function as stimuli that would control action, e.g. to maintain the level or rate of their occurrence when it drops substantially. Thus, I imagine the animal fed regularly at 24-hour intervals would have a different hunger 'drive', psychologically speaking, than the animal fed regularly at 12-hour intervals. That is, other things equal, the first might begin to show hunger behaviours after an interval of about 24 hours and the second at the end of 12 hours, although they might be equivalent in other ways, as in the amount of food they are given, and eat, regularly. If we overlook what may be an irrelevant fact that food or its equivalent is required for organismic survival, I suppose one could make the case that, in many of the important ways in which stimuli could acquire control over behaviours, food may be no different from any other functioning stimulus.

WOLFF *You remind me of the man who tried to train his horse not to eat. He almost succeeded just before the horse died.*

RHEINGOLD *I wonder if we shouldn't think more carefully before we use the term stimulus hunger. It is possible that we may be led to think of it as the same type of thing as hunger for food, which appears at certain intervals, can be satisfied more or less (although it wasn't in your family where they ate all the time), then abates for a period and so on. We are not sure that the infant's need for stimulation partakes of this character. It may not be cyclical. It may be that the more he gets the more he strives for, which would be different from eating. It may or may not be that his early experiences determine his later pattern. We assume that our early experiences with food modify our later appetites. We apply this to other modes, but we really don't know that we have babies that want visual, auditory and tactile stimulation. It is an attractive notion that should be explored but I am afraid that in using the term stimulus hunger we may miss something.*

WOLFF *By hunger I meant the sort of thing that Piaget calls 'aliment'.*

RHEINGOLD *Yes, and Gesell talks about visual experience being 'food' for an infant. It's a way we tend to think.*

AINSWORTH *I agree with you. I think too that Levy's term 'affect-hunger' is a bit off the track.*

ROWELL *Perhaps the word 'hunger' is relevant. We have a rather peculiar cultural idea of what hunger is. If you take a wider zoological view, there are not many animals which get hungry periodically and cyclically in the way that we do. Food is a much more time-consuming thing for many animals, they spend very little time* not *eating or sleeping.*

RHEINGOLD *Isn't it true that many animals that go out and hunt, eat and then do not hunt for maybe hours or days?*

ROWELL *A very few carnivores do that but most animals are picking around most of the time, eating a bit here and a bit there. Cows go on eating pretty steadily and there's not much of hunger in this cyclical way. People who deprive an animal of food for 24 hours are not producing a natural situation.*

GEWIRTZ *Even so, I would imagine that most animals eat periodically. Further, deprivation-satiation operations are involved in some of our most interesting and reliable behaviour laws, which hold in a variety of animal species; and these laws have been of considerable use for understanding basic aspects of animal behaviour and learning, whether or not long food deprivations are thought to produce a natural situation. In any event, there should always be recovery from the effects of having eaten. You are talking of the limiting case where the animal is taking in food at a regular rate, with deprivation and satiation conditions balancing each other out, as it were; but if there were any change in the availability of food in nature, as surely must happen occasionally to an animal individual or group and must have happened frequently in the history of every species, the typical consequences of deprivation-satiation operations would be seen in the animal's behaviours.*

ROWELL *Yes, but there isn't this attitude of 'I am hungry, I eat till I am full, and I stop and I wait until I am hungry again'.*

FOSS *Doesn't it depend on how many stomachs you have?*

GEWIRTZ *But that's one of the limits of the use of the concept.*

ROWELL *All I am saying is that food ingestion is much more variable than Harriet Rheingold was suggesting. There are some kinds of food hunger which look very much like Levy's 'affect-hunger'.*

GEWIRTZ *Yes, but I'm sure you have a situation involving food particularly, possibly other stimulus commodities as well, where, if the*

166

animal has been receiving food at a steady rate, he would be oriented minimally towards food; however, to the degree that the availability of food is cut down, he would become increasingly oriented towards that commodity. The fact that in certain naturally occurring situations an animal appears to be eating all the time, or that the lady Peter Wolff reported about drank tea continuously, might imply only that there is a range of settings in which operations falling in the direction of either end of the deprivation-satiation dimension would be likely to account minimally for variance in their behaviours with reference to food or water. And the greater portion of the variance in their behaviours might be a function of the particular conditions of their earlier learning, very much as an animal's preference to feed on earthworms or biscuits might be a function of such experimental learning. I think it is important to separate short-term operations, like those implementing 'hunger' and their reversible behavioural effects, from operations implemented through longer time spans, with cumulative effects like those indexed by the term 'affect-hunger'. As typically used, the term 'hunger' implies relationships holding only for a few hours or at most a few days between the availability of food and behaviours for food; the possibility of complete satiation after periodic deprivation is implied in its use, as are no residual effects that could cumulate to be manifested later for the earlier deficient events. Through short time spans, responsiveness to relevant stimuli would wax and wane as some function of the amount to which they were made available in the immediately preceding span of time. The use of the motivational concept 'hunger' would not be warranted to order relationships through long spans of time between the availability of stimuli like food and behaviours relevant to those stimuli. Learning concepts seem better suited to ordering, e.g. such effects as those of 'privation' or those termed 'affect-hunger', for these were evolved to order through the longer term systematic behaviour changes effected by recurring environmental conditions.

PART III

Method and Theory

Controlling the Infant's Exploratory Behaviour

HARRIET L. RHEINGOLD[1]

This is a brief report of some recent research on the effects of visual and auditory feedback upon the infant's exploratory behaviour. It is part of a programme in which information is sought about how the infant learns the nature of his environment, both social and non-social. The present work was planned with W. C. Stanley and carried out with the assistance of G. A. Doyle.

The specific proposition under test is that the infant's exploratory behaviour, in particular his manipulation of the environment, is modified by the stimulus properties and timing of the sensory feedback consequent upon that manipulation. The response of the infant chosen for study was touching a ball, a response assumed to belong to the class of exploratory behaviour. The consequence of touching the ball, that is, the response from the environment, was a short sequence of motion pictures accompanied by music. Modification was measured by changes in the rate of touching the ball. Would the infant's exploratory behaviour be modified by this response from the environment, if it were made contingent upon his own behaviour? Related questions were: 'Does combined visual and auditory stimulation function as a reinforcer for touching the ball?' and 'Can a connection be demonstrated in the young human infant between what the hand does and what the eyes see?'

The subjects were normal infants, three to six months of age, brought by their mothers to experimental rooms in the Clinical Centre of the National Institutes of Health. Plate 24 shows an infant in the apparatus, facing the screen and touching the ball. (The members of the Conference were shown a film of an infant performing in

[1] Laboratory of Psychology, National Institute of Mental Health, National Institutes of Health, Public Health Service, U.S. Department of Health, Education, and Welfare.

171

the apparatus.) Details of the method have been presented by Rhein-gold, Stanley, and Cooley (1962). Each time the infant touched the ball he activated a motion picture projector which showed brightly coloured paper cut-outs moving slowly across a dark background. In some trials, sequences of Swiss-music-box music were paired with the film.

To demonstrate that visual and auditory stimulation control the infant's touching of the ball, different experimental conditions have been used. These were a baseline condition (operant level), continuous and fixed-ratio schedules of reinforcement, non-contingent scheduling of the stimuli, and extinction.

In the non-contingent condition, used to control for a possible arousal effect, the stimuli appeared and disappeared not as a consequence of the infant's ball touching but on a schedule fixed by the experimenter. Extinction was used seldom, first, because it has meaning only if conditioning has been demonstrated – a state of affairs not easy to be sure of this early in the work – and, second, because it appeared to increase the fussiness of the infant.

Other factors which have been studied are the duration of the reinforcing stimuli, the duration of the experimental session, and the number of sessions. Thus, the duration of the movies and music has varied from $1\frac{1}{2}$ to 10 seconds. The experimental conditions have been of fixed durations or have been determined by the infant's performance. The number of sessions has varied from one to several.

The effects of some of these variables upon the infant's performance are illustrated by the records of two subjects. These are cumulative records: each time the infant touched the ball the recording pen made an upwards excursion; the pips to the left of the curve mark the onset of the reinforcer.

The first record (Fig. 17) shows the performance of a six-month-old infant in a session lasting 14 minutes. The reinforcing stimuli were 10 seconds of movies and music. Two experimental conditions were employed, continuous reinforcement and non-contingent stimulation. Under continuous reinforcement the rate of ball touching increased fairly regularly, minute by minute. When the slope appeared stable, at minute four, non-contingent scheduling was begun. The stimuli appeared for 10 seconds and disappeared for 10 seconds in regular alternation. Under this condition the rate of touching the ball became negatively accelerated. In the fifth minute continuous

172

reinforcement was reinstated, and an increase in performance occurred. The lag of only a minute or so in the infant's response to the
changed schedule demonstrates how sensitively the experimental conditions controlled his performance.

The use of other experimental procedures is demonstrated in the
cumulative records of a four-month-old infant (Fig. 18). In this
study, the duration of the sessions was fixed at 10 minutes, and a
different condition was used at each of three weekly sessions. In the

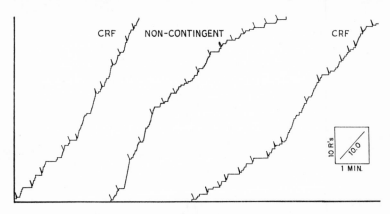

FIG. 17

*Cumulative response curve of an infant showing performance under the con-
tinuous reinforcement (CRF) and the non-contingent (NC) conditions.
Responses occurring during the 10 seconds of the reinforcer were recorded but
it was only the response after its conclusion which produced the next reinforcer*

first session, under the baseline condition, the infant touched the ball
65 times in irregular bursts. When non-contingent stimulation was
scheduled, that is, $1\frac{1}{2}$ seconds of motion pictures alternating with $2\frac{1}{2}$
seconds of no stimulation (sound did not accompany the visual
stimulation in this study), the number of responses was less than 40,
with long periods of no responding. Continuous reinforcement during the third session increased the number of responses to 215. The
experimental conditions appear to have modified the infant's performance.

To determine whether the levels of responding were specific to the
order of experimental conditions, other orders are being studied.

Although these particular curves suggest that sensory feedback of the nature used here can function as reinforcing stimuli and that the infant's behaviour was responsive to experimental control, similar success has not been obtained with all subjects. One of the major problems in experimental work with infants is adapting them to the unfamiliar situation of the laboratory. Lack of control over his ex-

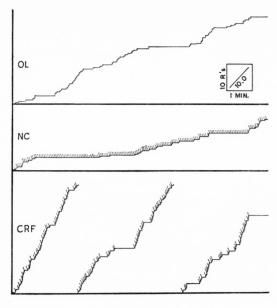

FIG. 18

Cumulative response curves of an infant showing performance under the operant level (OL), the continuous reinforcement (CRF), and the non-contingent (NC) conditions.

perience prior to study and the delicate problems posed by obtaining control are obvious. More specific to the present study is the problem presented by the high operant behaviour characteristic of some subjects. Touching the ball may be intrinsically reinforcing; it may offer tactile feedback which interferes with the programmed visual and auditory feedback. Further, the onset of visual and auditory feedback sometimes appears to disrupt the infant's touching the ball.

These and related problems should yield to further work. The goal is not necessarily to duplicate the learning curves characteristic of organisms of other species or ages. Rather it is to discover how the human infant behaves under specified conditions. To this end, work with different responses, different reinforcers, and with infants at different ages is in progress. The preliminary results, however, appear to demonstrate that sensory feedback can control the infant's exploratory behaviour.

Discussion following Dr Rheingold's contribution

FOSS *So far these infants have behaved as a rat would?*

RHEINGOLD *There are some marked differences. For example, the response we are studying does not need to be built up, step by step; it does not require shaping. The reason is that we have chosen a response natural to the organism in the situation in which he has been placed. Then, designing a situation that would keep the subject from fussing has been a concern. But to the extent that orderly changes in behaviour occur, we could say that the infants behaved like rats.*

GEWIRTZ *What happened when the infant responded while the reinforcing stimuli were on?*

RHEINGOLD *The responses were recorded on the cumulative record but did not affect the duration or the next onset of the reinforcing stimuli. It was the first response after the termination of the reinforcing stimuli which produced them again. It sometimes happened, however, that the response occurred so quickly after the termination of the reinforcer that the reinforcer appeared to stay on for longer than its fixed duration.*

GEWIRTZ *Did you change the duration of the reinforcing stimuli to one and one-half seconds for any special reason?*

RHEINGOLD *A long reinforcer permits more responses to go unreinforced than a short one. A short reinforcer might increase the likelihood of building an association between the response and its consequences. A limiting condition, however, is that the visual reinforcer should last long enough to present more than just a burst of light. The infant should be able to watch the figures move across the field.*

FOSS *Are you planning to use the situation in which the ball switches the film off, to parallel the rat experiments?*

RHEINGOLD *Not at present, but such a procedure should be tried. It would answer a question different from ours. Instead of asking whether the infant responds in order to increase stimulation in his universe, it asks whether he behaves to reduce it.*

BOWLBY *I was interested to hear you say that the infants cry during periods of extinction, that is, when they don't get the reward.*

RHEINGOLD *This has been our experience. Although extinction is an important procedure in the demonstration of learning, we have not used it frequently. Once the infant cries, he is removed from the apparatus, and naturally this early in the work we tend to avoid any condition which might increase the likelihood of fussiness.*

SCHAFFER *But the lag between the start of extinction and the start of crying might be an interesting measure, particularly if there were individual differences.*

RHEINGOLD *It would, indeed. At present, however, there are two complications. First, extinction as an experimental procedure has meaning only after conditioning has been demonstrated. This presents a limiting factor. Second, if extinction follows conditioning within the same session, the greater is the possibility that fatigue or some other factor besides just the absence of the reinforcer is responsible for the crying.*

AINSWORTH *Do any of these babies have similar sling seats at home?*

RHEINGOLD *Some do, others do not. In general, however, the seat resembles a type which must be in fairly common use, since we ordered it from a Montgomery Ward catalogue. It suits our purpose quite well as it holds the infant upright in a comfortable position.*

SCHAFFER *Did you say that the age range is between three and six months? I would think that three months was a bit young for behaviour of this kind, that is, reaching out and making contact with an object.*

RHEINGOLD *It is true that a three-month-old infant is not very proficient. Still, he will get his hands on the ball, however awkwardly. Much depends upon the positioning of the ball relative to the infant's reach. The position is adjusted for each infant. It must be neither so far away that making contact with it is difficult nor so near that he cannot avoid touching it. Nevertheless, as you suggest, we get better results with four-month-old infants.*

BOWLBY *Am I right in thinking that you are studying the behaviour at as early an age as is feasible?*

176

RHEINGOLD *Such is my purpose. Even more, it is my hope eventually to demonstrate that sensory feedback, or increased stimulation, of the kind used here, guides and controls exploratory behaviour in infants even younger than three months. For them a somewhat different response will have to be found, and the reinforcing stimuli will also require modification.*

BOWLBY *I was wondering what led you to choose three to six months in particular?*

RHEINGOLD *There is much in crib-side observation to suggest that at this age the frequency of a similar response, touching things, is regularly and promptly increased by the response the things touched provide the infant. Rattles, for example, move when touched and thus provide increased visual stimulation. If they also make sounds, they add a new sensory dimension. Further, some of these same stimulus properties are presented by the social objects, the persons in the infant's environment. As I suggested at our first conference, it is these properties which may both arouse and reinforce the smiling response in infants of this age.*

SCHAFFER *So to answer this question I presume you want to work away at different kinds of reinforcers and compare them.*

RHEINGOLD *It would be interesting to compare not only reinforcers of different sense modalities, alone and in combination, but also of such stimulus properties as complexity, novelty, and familiarity. By the use of motion pictures it should be possible to control for some of the visual dimensions. To that end we have made, but not yet used, a film of human faces.*

SCHAFFER *Do you think a face, as visually presented, in two dimensions, is recognized as a face at this early age?*

RHEINGOLD *I believe that there is no evidence yet to show whether an infant sees a film as three-dimensional. It may be that with his limited experience the real object and not a pictorial representation of it will be required.*

BOWLBY *If I understood Peter aright, even a good tape-recording of a voice was not responded to in the same way as the real voice.*

WOLFF *Stereo equipment, however, might have given better results.*

BOWLBY *But, as an example, an allegedly good representation didn't give quite as good a result. The film might also have its shortcomings.*

WOLFF *I have noticed that by two and a half months children become interested in television, particularly in the advertising.*

RHEINGOLD *A similar observation was made by Rudolph Schaffer yesterday about mothers who placed their infants near the radio. A television set might function as a surrogate mother for the human infant as a terry cloth cylinder did for Harry Harlow's monkeys.*

FOSS *I got the impression that the baseline measure, the operant level, was so high that the infant had to learn to slow down if he were to become efficient at the task. Any change in the situation, such as the onset of the film, would cause the rate of response to drop, at least in the beginning.*

RHEINGOLD *Your question raises several problems to which we have given considerable thought, but which still remain unsolved. First, not all infants have high baseline rates, and these subjects of course cause no problems. The first solution might therefore be to discard those with high rates. Second, if high baseline rates became slow steady ones following the onset of reinforcement, we would have evidence of some orderliness of response. At present we do not have a sufficient number of such records. Third, the high baseline rate could be reduced by making the ball less attractive; but it must be attractive enough to bring out the touching response.*

GEWIRTZ *Did there appear to be evidence of habituation in any of your response curves? Perhaps 10 minutes wasn't a long enough period to show it, but one does get habituation for the stimulus rapidly with single lights and similar stimulus events.*

RHEINGOLD *Habituation would be reflected in a decrease in the rate of response inversely proportional to the number of responses previously made. Certainly we have records in which the rate of response falls off. Sometimes these can be related directly to the experimental conditions, e.g. non-contingent stimulation or extinction. Other times fatigue or boredom or fussiness seem as likely explanations as habituation. What you say about single lights was verified by some preliminary work done with D. E. Berlyne last year. Panels lighted up red or green when touched by the infant. The rate of touching increased steadily over three days but fell to less than half on the fourth day.*

BOWLBY *Of course these films are much more interesting than the single light.*

Some Issues for Research in the Study of Attachment Behaviour

H. R. SCHAFFER

It is only recently that it has become possible to take the step from clinical speculation to the use of formal research techniques in the study of the formation and development of social attachments in infancy. Bowlby's (1958) theoretical analysis has done much to stimulate our thinking about this area, and the most urgent need we are now facing is for the systematic collection of empirical data in order to define the relevant phenomena and the conditions under which they take place.

The first problem confronting the investigator in a relatively new area of research is to decide in what direction he should turn his attention, what aspects of the subject are likely to be most fruitful, and what variables he should select for detailed study. Theory is one guide in such a quest, exploratory research another, and it is mainly to the latter that I shall turn here. What I intend to do in this paper is to carry out a conducted tour through this area in order to point out some of its significant features and to examine those issues which appear to me most worthy of further study. As signposts on this trip I shall use some findings obtained in the course of a longitudinal study on the social behaviour of a group of 60 infants during the first 12 months of life, which was designed to ascertain some of the conditions under which a child forms his first attachment to another person.[1] The details of this investigation will be reported at a later date: here I have abstracted those impressions and preliminary results which appear to be relevant to our present concern.

[1] I am much indebted to Mrs Peggy Emerson for her help in the execution of this project.

The assessment of attachment behaviour

The finding of suitable operational criteria has always been a task of particular difficulty in the field of interpersonal relationships, and the attachment phenomenon is no exception in this respect.

As one's choice of a criterion will depend to a considerable extent on the way in which the phenomenon is conceptualized, I shall turn to this problem first of all and briefly discuss how we might best approach it.

To form any kind of relationship to an object, human or otherwise, is clearly impossible unless self and non-self, subject and object, have become differentiated. It is for this reason that I have elsewhere (Schaffer, 1958) drawn attention to the relevance which Piaget's (1955) formulations about the growth of the object concept have for studies of social development in infancy. In the early months, Piaget argues, an object as an independent, permanent substance cannot as yet be conceived by the infant, as for him there exist only fleeting images which may be recognized but which have no existence apart from his own activity. In the infant's world the fundamental units are not the distinct entities which the adult mind knows, but are represented by as yet unco-ordinated schema in which the relevent environmental attributes are assimilated to the organism's needs. An object is thus not considered as an entity in its own right but only as a functional element: not as a dummy or a rattle but as something to be sucked or something to be shaken. Being tied to the infant's immediate needs and activities there cannot as yet be any conservation of the object, and once the object is outside the immediate perceptual field the infant behaves as though it has ceased to exist.

Piaget was, of course, only concerned with cognitive development, yet the same psychological apparatus that deals with dummies and rattles also deals with maternal breasts and grandmothers. The social object too may be said to have no existence initially apart from action and not to be missed in its absence, so that, as we have shown in an earlier study of infants' reactions to hospitalization (Schaffer and Callender, 1959), there is relatively little difficulty in the early months in exchanging the mother for an unfamiliar caretaker. As his criterion for the beginnings of object conservation Piaget used the infant's orientation towards a missing object, and the parallel development of social and non-social objects is strikingly illustrated by

180

the fact that we found upset on separation from the mother to begin just at the same age that Piaget's infants began searching for objects that had been removed from the perceptual field. Both instances may be said to provide evidence that a permanent object with an independent existence external to the subject has been constructed. The infant after this point is no longer willing to accept *any* environmental attribute that will satisfy his needs but will search until he has found the particular toy or person that now forms the *specific* object of his need.

It is for this reason that in our previous work we found separation upset to be such a useful indication that some kind of permanent relationship to the mother had been established. The hospitalization situation highlights the new discriminative element in the child's social development, for the child is now no longer care-oriented (irrespective of the source of care) but person-oriented, and the absence of the familiar person will in itself elicit strong protests. When the physical proximity of a particular individual is sought in its own right an attachment may be said to have been formed to that individual, and to test for this occurrence one may best observe the child's behaviour in conditions where he is prevented from attaining such proximity.

In our longitudinal study we were, of course, not able to use the hospitalization situation and had therefore to look for another, comparable index which could be repeatedly applied at recurring intervals throughout the course of the first 12 months. Again we studied separation responses, but this time selected those separation situations which occur in the everyday life of all children. After some preliminary investigations we drew up a list of seven such situations which appeared to be of almost universal occurrence in the population investigated, and our inquiries therefore centred on what happens when an infant is left alone in a room, when he is left with other people, when the adult passes by his cot or chair without picking him up, when he is put down after a period on the adult's knee, when he is put outside the house in his pram, when he is left outside shops, and when he is left in his cot at night. The break in contact observed in these situations may be much briefer and less traumatic than that found in the hospital situation: nevertheless, it does contain the same element of loss of the familiar figure through her disappearance from the perceptual field. By rating the intensity of a child's protests on a four-point scale for each of these situations and then combining the scores, an indication of the total intensity of attachment may be obtained. We collected the relevant information through interviews held with the mothers at four-weekly intervals throughout the major part of the first year, and were thus able to trace the growth and formation of attachment behaviour.

The initial formation of specific attachments

Attention had first to be paid to the problem of defining the attachment phenomenon, for the choice of one's criterion will, of course, influence the nature of the results obtained. We can now turn to the second problem, namely the age when a child first becomes capable of forming attachments to particular individuals.

In Table 8 the results are presented of a preliminary analysis of the first 23 of our infants whose follow-up period has been completed. By determining for each infant the four-weekly period during which the first sign of specific attachment occurred (i.e. the age when protests directed at a specific individual in any of the seven separation situations were first manifested), a distribution is obtained the mode of which is located in the seventh lunar month and which indicates clearly the third quarter of the first year as the critical age range for the emergence of this particular function.

TABLE 8

Age at formation of first specific attachment and at emergence of fear of strangers

Lunar month	Attachment N	Fear of strangers N
6	1	0
7	9	2
8	5	8
9	4	8
10	2	4
11	1	0
12	1	0
13 plus	0	1

These results confirm the findings of our hospitalization study, for there too separation upset was observed to occur as from seven months. Let me hastily add, however, that to determine the relevant age range is but a beginning of one's inquiry and not the end. The function of the age variable is merely to direct our attention to a certain phase of development; it cannot by itself provide us with any clue as to *why* this function emerges just at this time, i.e. what processes are responsible for its occurrence. To this challenging problem we have as yet no definite answer, yet it is worth commenting that all the evidence points to the third quarter of the first year as a most important turning point in early development. Piaget's sensori-motor stage IV, which marks the beginnings of object conservation, first manifests itself at this time, and also at this age one aspect of social behaviour which has been intensively studied in its own right, namely the smiling response, has been found to undergo certain fundamental changes. Spitz (1946) has described how in the first six months the smile is released by a gestalt signal as represented by certain superficial attributes possessed by all humans, so that smiling occurs indiscriminately to all presentations of the necessary stimuli. It is only after this age, i.e. in the third quarter of the first year, that the infant will cease to smile at primitive configurational properties and respond instead to certain familiar people and not to unfamiliar ones. All the investigations thus show that soon after six months the infant reaches a higher-level stage of responsiveness at which he no longer mechanically reacts to a set range of attributes in the here-and-now, but that he becomes capable at this age of conceptualizing (at a primitive level) the objects and individuals of his environment and of exercising a higher degree of selectivity in responding to them.

It is apparent that our 'seven-months phenomenon' is but one expression of a more general development, which still awaits detailed definition. There is, however, one finding which may help to clarify the manner of onset of attachment behaviour. Included in our investigation was an inquiry as to the development of fear of strangers, based on the child's reactions to the approach of the interviewer. The age when fear responses were first observed is shown in Table 8 side-by-side with the data regarding the onset of specific attachment behaviour, demonstrating that the two functions do not arise simultaneously but that the mode of the fear distribution occurs about a month after that of the attachment distribution. The tendency to seek the company of familiar individuals and the tendency to avoid the company of strangers cannot therefore be regarded as merely the opposite sides of the same coin. This conclusion is further reinforced by the fact that the intensities of the two phenomena do not necessarily coincide, for an infant may show a high degree of attachment to certain specific individuals and yet very little fear of strangers, or, alternatively, he may have considerable fear of strangers but show only minimal signs of attachment. We are dealing, therefore, with two distinct functions which may eventually come to interact with one another but which require separate examination, each in its own right.

The intensity of attachment behaviour

Once an attachment has been established to a specific individual, its intensity will vary from child to child. In Fig. 19 the individual attachment curves of four infants are reproduced, together with the fear-of-stranger curves, in order to illustrate some of the individual differences that may occur. These figures also illustrate the considerable fluctuations from month to month that may sometimes be observed for any one infant, and the frequency with which such dramatic changes were reported indicates that, within the age range studied here, both attachment and fear are still far from being steady and stable phenomena.

That children differ in the extent to which they can tolerate brief separations from the mother is a matter of common knowledge. We are, however, still largely ignorant as to the factors which account for these individual differences. Investigators concerned with this problem may adopt any one of the following three points of view in their search for an answer: (1) The intensity of attachment is a function of certain internal characteristics of the child, these giving rise to certain forms of behaviour to which the adults in his environment must adjust. (2) The intensity of attachment is a function of the social environment of the child which stimulates and fosters his attachment behaviour. (3) The intensity of attachment is the resultant of forces emanating from both child and environment.

Looking through our data, we have found evidence that seems to support both of the first two possibilities. On the one hand, children often do seem to dictate their parents' behaviour by the insistence of their demands, for quite a number of the mothers we interviewed reported that they were forced to respond far more than they considered desirable, that they had to 'give in' despite their belief that the child might thereby become 'spoiled'. Certain temporary conditions in particular, such as illness, tiredness, pain, etc., appear to intensify

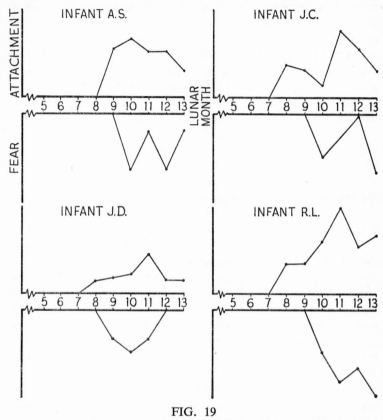

FIG. 19

The development of specific attachments and of fear of strangers in four individual infants

the child's demands for the mother's presence, and in addition there appear to be many spontaneous fluctuations in attachment intensity which are quite unrelated to variations in maternal behaviour. On the other hand, parents are far from passive beings entirely at the mercy of their children's demands, for many have strong views on the amount of attention a child should be given and do their best to make the child conform to these views. The most extreme example of the part which the social environment plays is provided by institutionalized infants who fail altogether to develop attachment behaviour, but amongst our infants too there are many instances showing that attachment responses may or may not be reinforced by the action of the environment. This is particularly clearly indicated by the manner in which a child will select one person rather than another as the object of his attachment behaviour in a given situation: several of our infants, for example, invariably cried after father when he passed by yet never after mother, for they had presumably learned that the former tended to give way to their demands for attention quite readily whereas mother had consistently refused to do so for fear of 'spoiling'.

The very fact that both these alternatives are supported by data leads us to the third possibility. Middlemore's (1941) study of the neonate's feeding response, so appropriately entitled *The Nursing Couple*, showed clearly that mutual adaptation must take place from the very beginning of mother-infant interaction, and it would be difficult to escape the conclusion that in the case of attachment behaviour too a reciprocal arrangement is indicated. The details of interaction in this area remain to be spelled out; in the meantime the most likely explanation would appear to be that the tendency a child has to attach itself to specific individuals will manifest itself at a certain developmental phase under suitable environmental conditions at an intensity which will vary from child to child, and that it will then give rise to a number of behavioural cues to which the mother and others will respond in a characteristic fashion, thereby further influencing the course of the attachment behaviour. The eventual intensity of the attachment depends therefore both on the strength of that particular child's need and the extent to which the people around him are prepared to satisfy it. The 'nursing couple', we may conclude, has become the 'attachment couple'.

The objects of attachment behaviour

When talking about a young child's attachment behaviour there is an assumption which is probably in the minds of us all but which ought to be made explicit and examined in the light of empirical findings. The assumption is that initially the child's attachment will be with one person only, that this person will always be the mother, and that

186

it is therefore only the mother-child relationship with which we need be concerned. In the course of collecting our data it has become abundantly clear, however, that the situation is by no means always as clear-cut as this formulation would suggest.

In the first place, we have encountered very few instances where the mother is the *only* person to whom the infant under 12 months shows attachment behaviour. From the very beginning of this particular phase of development it appears to be the rule rather than the exception that several individuals are selected as the objects of the infant's attachment responses, that protest at being left in one or another of the separation situations investigated by us is evoked by a number of persons and not just by one. There are several possibilities: each of the various individuals involved may act as the child's attachment object in a different separation situation, with no overlap occurring; or all the individuals serve as objects of attachment in all the separation situations that evoke protest; or some situations will call forth attachment behaviour directed at only one particular individual while others will elicit it from a number of individuals.

In the second place, the mother is not always the person to whom attachment behaviour is shown most frequently and intensely. More often than not she is, admittedly, to be found at the top of the child's hierarchy of objects of attachment, but there are cases where other people are selected for this position even though the total amount of time that they spend with the child each day may be very much less. One of our most striking examples is provided by the infant who showed far more intense attachment behaviour towards the ten-year old girl living next door than towards the members of his own family – despite the much greater availability of his parents, and despite the fact that the neighbour's daughter never fed him and rarely cuddled him (but she did carry him around a great deal!).

To concentrate only on the child-mother relationship would therefore be misleading and artificial. Indeed, I feel we can probably learn most about the nature of the attachment process by taking into account all the people in the child's environment and by carrying out a careful analysis of what it is that prompts an infant to select one person rather than another as the object of his attachment under given circumstances. In this way it should be easier to isolate the stimulus properties which evoke the attachment responses of an infant.

Up till now we have concerned ourselves only with the formation of *specific* attachments. Yet what occurs in the third quarter of the first year is by no means the emerging of a completely new form of behaviour, for already in the first six months social attachment is shown by the infant's reluctance to be left alone by other people. But whereas after seven months the child's crying is set off by the departure of only certain specific individuals, before that time it appears that the company of *anybody*, familiar or stranger, will satisfy the child. Thus the ten-month-old infant will cry when his mother leaves him, say, in his pram outside the house, will often remain oriented towards the door through which she disappeared, will not stop crying when a stranger comes up to comfort him but on the contrary may cry all the more, and will only quieten when the mother (or some other specific familiar individual) reappears. The five-month-old infant may also cry when left in this situation, but he, on the contrary, will quieten as soon as any passer-by approaches and interacts with him, will then quickly become responsive and cheerful, only to be upset once more when the stranger departs. In both infants a definite need is indicated, and in both this need becomes apparent under similar circumstances – namely when social isolation takes place. In one case, however, the infant will be satisfied only by the presence of one or two particular individuals, whereas in the other case it is attention from anyone that appears to be sought. What takes place after seven months is, therefore, not a change in the nature of the behaviour pattern but a change in the evoking stimuli. The infant is no longer oriented towards people as a class, but has narrowed the range of objects to whom he shows attachment behaviour to just one or two selected individuals. Two phases of social development are thus indicated: a phase of *indiscriminate* attachment and a phase of *specific* attachment.

All the infants in our longitudinal study showed indiscriminate attachment before they formed a specific attachment, and it seems to me that in the former phenomenon we have an essential precondition for the development of the latter. This point can, however, be demonstrated more clearly by turning to another investigation that we are conducting at present, which is concerned with the effects of long-term separation on the subsequent establishment of specific attachments. Although the study is not yet completed, certain quite clear-cut results are emerging that are relevant here.

The sample is comprised of two groups who differ in the nature of their separation experience. One of these (the 'Hospital group', as we shall refer to it here) was obtained from a children's hospital, where the total amount of stimulation, both social and otherwise, received by these infants was limited. This environment has been described in somewhat greater detail elsewhere (Schaffer, 1958), and may be said to give rise to a condition of 'perceptual monotony' for these infants. When social interaction did take place it might be with any one of a number of nurses, few of whom stayed for long periods in a particular ward. The 11 infants of this group were, however, visited by their mothers, this being once a week for the majority but several times a week in three of the cases. In Table 9 the relevant details are given, including the length of the infants' stay in hospital and their age when discharged home. For the purpose of this presentation I am considering only those infants who were at least 30 weeks old at the time of reunion with their families, i.e. those who might, under normal circumstances, be considered ready for the formation of a specific attachment.

The other group (to be referred to here as the 'Baby Home group') had been admitted to an institution because of contact with tuberculosis, necessitating B.C.G. vaccination. There were nine infants in this group, and their mean length of separation did not differ significantly from that of the Hospital group (see Table 9). The age range at time of discharge is also comparable. The nature of their separation experience, on the other hand, differed in two important respects: in the first place no visiting was allowed in the Baby Home and no contact whatever occurred therefore with the mother throughout the course of these infants' stay, and in the second place the amount of stimulation that the Baby Home group received during the separation was far greater than that received by the Hospital group. This was mainly because the ratio of staff to children was very much higher in the Baby Home, with the result that a quite considerable amount of social interaction was experienced by these infants. In the Baby Home too, however, no infant was looked after by any one particular nurse acting as mother-substitute, care being provided indiscriminately by a large number of nurses.

After each infant's return home the course of his attachment behaviour was plotted, using the measures already described. The last column for each group in Table 9 gives the time lag in days between return home and the appearance of the first sign of a specific

TABLE 9

The formation of specific attachments by infants of 30 weeks and over following discharge from two separation environments

HOSPITAL GROUP

Infant	Age at discharge (weeks)	Length of separation (weeks)	Amount of visiting (per week)	Time lag for appearance of specific attachment (days)
L. C.	31	30	Once	83
J. B.	31	17	Once	—*
W. C.	34	27	Four times	41
J. C.	34	11	Once	98
L. McF.	34	10	Five times	33
G. C.	37	11	Once	45
C. F.	39	26	Once	39
W. McN.	39	10	Once	28
J. D.	41	24	Once	51
R. C.	41	14	Five times	10
W. B.	46	17	Once	34
Mean:	36·9	17·9		55·0*

BABY HOME GROUP

Infant	Age at discharge (weeks)	Length of separation (weeks)	Amount of visiting (per week)	Time lag for appearance of specific attachment (days)
J. McL.	30	17	None	13
I. R.	30	12	None	47
J. B.	35	29	None	5
A. T.	35	13	None	5
L. M.	36	13	None	3
A. I.	36	12	None	84
M. D.	37	11	None	14
T. R.	45	22	None	3
B. D.	52	37	None	3
Mean:	37·3	18·4		19·7

* Infant J. B. had at the end of his first year still not formed any specific attachments. For the purpose of calculating the mean time lag of his group the figure of 143 has been arbitrarily used, this being the number of days between his discharge and his first birthday. The mean figure given is thus likely to be a conservative estimate.

attachment. A striking contrast is provided here between the two groups. The Baby Home group established a specific attachment to the mother far more quickly than the Hospital group – despite the fact that none of the former infants had had any contact whatever with the mother, whereas all the hospitalized infants saw their mothers at least once a week throughout their stay. The difference between the two groups in this respect reaches a statistical significance level of ·02 (Mann-Whitney test), the means of the distributions being 55·0 and 19·7 days respectively. More telling than group averages, however, are the individual scores of the infants. In the Hospital group all but one infant took at least four weeks to establish a specific attachment, two took approximately three months to do so, and one infant had still not shown any specific attachment behaviour by the time he reached the end of the first year. In the Baby Home group, on the other hand, five of the nine infants developed a specific attachment within five days of returning home and two others did so within the second week. There are two exceptions to this general trend, and these I shall discuss presently.

These data suggest that a prolonged acquaintance with the individual(s) with whom a specific attachment is eventually formed is less essential than the total amount of prior social stimulation received by the infant, irrespective of the source. In the Baby Home a great deal of interaction took place between the infant and his caretakers, and while conditions did not lend themselves to the formation of a specific attachment, a generalized need for social stimulation was fostered. It was this, we must assume, which enabled the infants to establish a specific bond fairly speedily once the environment did supply a constant mother-figure. The Hospital infants, however, had not experienced anything but a minimum of social stimulation, and before being able to form any specific attachments these infants had first to go through a phase of indiscriminate attachment behaviour. This took place in all 11 members of this group after their return home, occurring generally within a fairly brief period of this event. It is as though these infants had been kept in cold storage during their hospitalization and after their discharge had first to recapitulate a developmental phase through which they should have passed had they been reared all along under normal conditions, before being able to reach the next phase in their social development. An essential precondition, we may conclude, to which attention must be paid by the research worker concerned with the formation of specific attachments, is the level of social stimulation as experienced by the infant in the previous developmental phase.

One more precondition is highlighted by returning to the two cases amongst the Baby Home group which had exceptionally long time lags. One of these (I.R.) showed no unusual features which might account for the delay, and the only explanation which I can offer is that this infant would have been a late developer anyway. The other case (A.I.) is, however, more instructive. On his return home this child was looked after by his invalid father, who had to stay at home while the mother went out to work. Both parents were fond of the child, but because of his condition the father was unable to give the child anything but the minimum of care and stimulation, while the mother saw the child for only brief periods each day. Two and a half months after the infant's return home, however, the mother gave up work and devoted all her time to her family, and within a few days the child had developed a strong specific attachment centred exclusively on the mother.

This case illustrates vividly the interacting influence of organismic and environmental variables. Whatever the nature of the present environment, an infant can hardly form a specific attachment until certain organismic changes have taken place. But once this stage has been reached another condition becomes necessary, namely the availability in his environment of the right kind of stimuli, i.e. the presence of one or two main caretakers providing the required amount of stimulation.

Developmental antecedents of attachment behaviour

A definite though indiscriminate orientation towards social objects may thus be said to antedate the formation of specific attachments. Are we to conclude then that some kind of social drive as such exists from the very beginning?

It is my impression (and I cannot at present put it any more strongly) that a still earlier phase may be discerned, in that the need for social stimulation arises from the need for stimulation. The infant who at ten months cries for his mother and who at five months cried for the attention of any person, will have cried at three months for almost any form of environmental change.

192

I am encouraged to make these remarks by the fact that Harriet Rheingold (1961) has also been led to such a conclusion by her data. A searching of the environment for stimulation is, to her mind, one of the most prominent characteristics of the young infant, and nowhere does this become as obvious as in the separation situations around which our inquiry centred. It is not only (as Rheingold has rightly pointed out) that human beings in themselves form the most stimulating part of the infant's environment, but also that the supply of non-social stimulation too is usually dependent on the adult. The young infant's motor equipment does not at first enable him to produce all those interesting sights and sounds which he needs to relieve his boredom, for in the early months he cannot even effect a change in position in order to bring about a change in visual perspective. When, therefore, the adult disappears and leaves him to his own devices the infant will have only very limited means at his disposal to produce some form of entertainment, and under these circumstances his natural reaction is to cry. The three-month-old baby, left in the garden facing a blank brick wall, will begin to cry within a fairly short time; if he is then put under a tree where he can watch the leaves moving about in the wind peace will reign once more. Stimulation-producing devices such as this are in fact commonly employed by mothers in order to stop or prevent their babies' crying, and in the course of our investigation we have come across quite a large number of these. The provision of toys is perhaps the most common example but there are others of a less usual character. One of our mothers, for instance, found the most effective way of keeping her baby quiet was to switch on her vacuum cleaner, while another claimed that her infant would only settle in his cot if the radiogram was on. Still another mother used a tape-recorder: at first it was sufficient for the infant merely to watch it going round and round, but after a while he became bored with this and the sound had to be switched on. Several of our infants were said to cry unless the television set was on – with the advertisements acting as particularly effective eyecatchers! More common examples are provided by pram rocking, by wheeling or carrying the child around from place to place, by putting him next to vividly patterned curtains (especially when these are moving in the wind), by leaving the light on at night, by placing the child in a chair where he can examine the design of the cushions or of the wall-paper, or by leaving his pram at the front of the house where there is traffic to be watched and listened to rather than at the back where all is quiet.

In carrying out such an inquiry it soon becomes obvious that right from the beginning the infant is no mere passive being to whom nothing matters but food and warmth. Whatever label will eventually be found most appropriate for the tendency we are now discussing – stimulus hunger, curiosity, arousal seeking, exploratory drive – it seems likely that this function is one of the most important attributes with which a child comes into the world. That the organism is in very real need of environmental stimulation is by now a well accepted notion (Hebb (1955), Thompson (1955), Berlyne (1960) and others have elaborated this point), but there is one further aspect which needs emphasizing in view of the bearing it has on mother-infant interaction, namely that this tendency, like all other characteristics of an organism, may be found to different degrees in different individuals.

The existence of individual differences in the function under discussion is one of the most striking features which emerges from our material. There are, on the one hand, babies who seem satisfied with very little stimulation, who can be left to their own devices for long periods under relatively monotonous conditions, who rarely cry for environmental change and whose orientation towards the outside world appears to be minimal. These infants are usually described as 'easy' and 'content', for they make few demands on their caretakers. There are, on the other hand, babies who appear simply ravenous for stimulation, who cry most readily at its lack, and where mothering entails an almost continuous supply of one form or another of excitation. As the mother of one such baby once put it to me: 'When I take him out for a walk in the park, he just will not lie in his pram like all the other babies. He has to be propped up so that he can see everything that is going on, the hood has to be left down in case he misses anything, and the moment the pram stops he begins to cry.'

If we are to accept the notion that the optimal amount of stimulation differs from infant to infant, then we may further hypothesize that it is a function of mothering to supply this optimal amount. Mothers are likely to differ in their sensitivity in this respect and in the degree to which they are prepared to respond to the infant's signals, so that it should become possible to range them along a continuum from high responsiveness ('I cannot bear to hear my baby cry and have to pick him up the moment he starts') to low respon-

194

siveness ('I think a baby should never be picked up between feeds, and when I hear mine cry just for attention I simply leave him to it'). Mutual adaptation is once again the keynote, and where this does not take place a pathological relationship may well be indicated. This may take the form either of understimulation or overstimulation, and it is worth noting in passing that while we now know quite a lot about the effects of understimulation (thanks mainly to studies of institutionalized babies), we still know almost nothing about the effects of overstimulation.

Just how a mother's behaviour affects the infant's development at this early age is a vast area which is still almost completely uncharted. The main obstacle to progress is that the relevant parameters of maternal behaviour remain yet to be identified, for what constitutes relevance will differ from one developmental phase to the next. Thus it is unlikely that many of the factors believed to be important in later childhood (Baldwin *et al.*, 1949, Sears *et al.*, 1957) will be significant determinants of infant behaviour; whereas the over-all quantity of stimulation is likely to play a much more important part in the early months than at any subsequent time.

I do not, of course, wish to maintain that the quantitative aspect of stimulation is the only significant feature in mother-infant interaction. This was made very clear to us when we came to examine the manner of interaction and (under the impact of Professor Harlow's (1959) ideas) gave particular attention to the part which physical contact plays in this respect. We were surprised to find that a strikingly large proportion of our infants were reported as disliking physical contact in the form of cuddling, hugging, kissing, etc., and that these infants much preferred to relate to their mothers through visual and auditory means. We shall report separately on these infants at a later date: here I merely wish to point out that once again a problem of mutual adaptation is involved. Anyone who has ever observed the sensuous manner in which many mothers fondle their babies will appreciate that a mother too may have a contact need, and when such a mother is matched with a non-cuddling baby a considerable challenge is held out to her adaptability. If she does not have the ability to relate to the baby in other ways and perhaps interprets the situation as a rejection by the infant of herself, another source of a pathological relationship may be indicated. Thus not only the amount but also the nature of stimulation is of consequence.

195

This earliest stage, we may conclude, is essentially an a-social one, in which other human beings are not yet sought after in their own right as distinct from vacuum cleaners and tape-recorders. But, as Harriet Rheingold (1961) has pointed out so clearly, the infant soon learns that social objects have a much higher stimulating value than the inanimate part of the environment, that they are both more interesting and more responsive and thus much more satisfying. Herein, I suggest, lie the origins of attachment behaviour: having learned of the special stimulating properties inherent in his human partners, the infant begins to distinguish them as a class in their own right, seeks their physical proximity in order to be exposed to their relatively high (but also accommodating) arousal value, and protests when he is prevented from achieving this end. A three-stage hypothesis regarding the formation of attachment behaviour seems therefore justified: an early phase in which optimal arousal is sought from all parts of the environment precedes a phase where the infant, having learned that social objects provide the best sources of such stimulation, shows indiscriminate attachment behaviour to all human beings, and this finally gives way to the phase with which we are best acquainted, namely the phase of specific attachments.

Conclusions

What, then, are the main issues which confront the research worker in this area? There are, I believe, three problems to which, in the present state of knowledge, particular attention must be given.

In the first place, it is necessary to confirm the three-stage hypothesis advanced above, i.e. to ascertain whether the relevant phenomena stand in the sequential order which I have indicated.

Secondly, the processes and variables responsible for the passage from one stage to the next must be defined. Some of these have already been suggested, but the conditions necessary for attaining the seven-months developmental milestone in particular are in need of further study.

And finally, the individual differences observed at all points of the developmental sequence call for explanation. This will, amongst other things, entail a closer definition of the relevant characteristics of the social environment, so that one may ascertain to what extent these are linked to differences in infant behaviour.

Discussion following paper by Dr Schaffer

ROBERTSON *This is a very interesting suggestion – that the infant does not necessarily show a preference for the mother?*

SCHAFFER *In some cases the most intense attachment is shown to somebody other than the mother, and in a few cases several people (who may or may not include the mother) are equally preferred.*

BOWLBY *It moves from an indefinite range of persons to a limited range which may be anything from one to half a dozen or so?*

SCHAFFER *Yes. After the indiscriminate phase, during which the infant's range of object encompasses all human beings with whom he comes into contact under the relevant conditions, a narrowing down takes place, and from about seven months on only specific attachments are formed. There appears to be, however, no inherent mechanism in the infant which insists that initially attachments must be formed to* one *person only. This depends entirely on the learning opportunities held out to the infant in his particular social environment. In most cases the mother is at the top of the hierarchy, but not* necessarily *so. Let me repeat the example which I mentioned earlier, where the ten-year-old girl living next door was the main object of attachment – although she did not take any part in the infant's physical care and was available for far less time than the mother. I do believe that we are going to learn most about the nature of attachments by carrying out a careful analysis of all these various objects and the different kinds of stimulation which they offer the infant, instead of simply isolating the mother-child relationship and concentrating on this to the exclusion of all else.*

ROBERTSON *With regard to this child's preference for the ten-year-old, are these direct observations of yours, or reported to you?*

SCHAFFER *It was entirely based on interview material obtained from the mother. Although this may, of course, introduce certain biases, we have carried out reliability checks by making comparisons with our own observations which suggest that the degree of distortion is really very limited.*

HARLOW *As this child grew older did the mother become the primary love object?*

SCHAFFER *Not by the time that the child had reached 12 months of age. I can't tell you what happened after that.*

MICHELL *If instead of using as an indicator the distress shown by a child at separation you had used 'to whom does the child go for comfort when he is upset', do you think you would have got the same hierarchy of attachments?*

SCHAFFER *I can't give you any definite answer about that because we confined ourselves to collecting data about the one criterion only. We studied this because it has certain practical as well as conceptual advantages, and it is a matter for further research to ascertain the correlation between this and other indexes.*

APPELL *Do you have any ideas about the other ways of showing attachment that the child may use towards the mother, by making signs of attachment other than protest or by holding arms up to her and things like that?*

SCHAFFER *I think there is a great range of behaviour which may be quoted here, but our concern was to study the attachment function as a whole, using one particular operational definition for this purpose, and not to analyse the various behaviour patterns through which attachments are expressed.*

APPELL *My point is that in those infants where you haven't seen any protest, there might have been other signs of attachment.*

SCHAFFER *That is why an investigation of this nature depends entirely on the particular measures which it uses for purposes of assessment. In our previous cross-sectional study of the effect of hospitalization in the first year we were so much struck by the ability of the separation criterion to differentiate infants that we wanted to use it in this longitudinal study too. Separations at home, of course, take place under far less dramatic circumstances, and this means that the measure may be rather less sensitive. All this scale can do is to differentiate the sample in terms of the particular operational definition used, and this is all that can be claimed at the present juncture.*

APPELL *Then you also mentioned that this boy with the ten-year-old neighbour was very much carried around in a pram by her so maybe he was attached to the situation of being carried in a pram. Perhaps she was attached to the total situation rather than the girl herself.*

FOSS *In those cases where an infant was left alone, might he have preferred a doll or rattle or something? I mean, did you control that? I imagine the situation would be very different when he had nothing of that kind with him from when he did.*

SCHAFFER *It certainly made a difference, to some infants at any rate, whether they were left alone with something that distracted them or not. In general, the circumstances in which the separation took place often had a marked effect on the infant's response – whether he was occupied with toys, whether a sibling was left with him, whether he was feeling tired or poorly at the time, etc. These extraneous factors were not controlled in the sense of being held constant or in any way experimentally manipulated, for we were concerned more with naturally occurring situations and behaviour. But we did always inquire about the effects of such conditions and took them into account both in scoring on the attachment scale and in our qualitative analysis. In so far as our inquiry encompassed not just one particular instance but all the relevant behaviour which had taken place in the preceding month, we obtained an over-all picture in which all these conditions were represented.*

The Concept of a Critical Period for the Development of Social Responsiveness in Early Human Infancy

J. A. AMBROSE

Introduction

The issue I would like to raise for discussion is that of whether or not there is a critical or sensitive period in the development of the social responsiveness of the human being. I am doing this firstly as an inevitable outcome of the recent rapid growth of interest in this subject pertaining to animals at several phyletic levels. While admittedly the claims made in many instances have tended to outstrip the evidence on which they have been based, the accumulation of more carefully controlled experiments on imprinting has made it increasingly clear that certain types of events occurring over brief and relatively fixed periods shortly after birth can have relatively stable effects on the later social responsiveness of the individual. Such work is only in the early stages; the nature and extent of the effects of imprinting need a lot more study: though species and individual differences are apparent, the nature of the factors affecting these and indeed of the sorts of mechanism subserving the process itself have yet to be spelled out. Nevertheless the very fact of the phenomenon probably at various phyletic levels, however inadequately understood as yet, makes it not only plausible to ask if anything resembling it operates at the human level, but suggests it is also of the greatest practical importance that we do so. For if anything of such a nature is found, its implications for preventive psychiatry appear to be far-reaching.

Another reason for raising the issue is a cautionary one. Matching the importance of the issue is its complexity and difficulty. Consequently there are many pitfalls in such an inquiry at the human level

201

and, before attempts in this direction go too far, I think it is timely that we should try to clarify both the nature of the issue and also what would constitute evidence for or against the hypothesis that there is an early critical period in the development of human social responsiveness. Already there has been a number of passing suggestions, and at least one serious attempt to demonstrate, that imprinting operates in human infancy. While these undoubtedly manifest breadth of vision, they mostly suffer from perhaps an excess of enthusiasm which tends to encourage a positive conclusion which goes far beyond the evidence available. Part of the difficulty here too seems to be the genuine problem for both animal ethologists and human psychologists of gaining a close enough acquaintance with and understanding of the data, methods and limitations of each other.

Since the group assembled here this week is a concentration of people with specialized knowledge of this early period either in human or animal infancy and including some who are familiar with the phenomena of imprinting and with its methodological problems, the main thing I want to do is to encourage it to bring to bear its collective resources on the problem of clarifying the issue of imprinting considered in relation to human infancy.

There is neither time nor, I believe for this group, necessity to start by referring to Lorenz's (1935) original findings and claims about imprinting and by outlining the many directions in which subsequently these have been either extended, modified or clarified. It is obviously important that we reach a clear idea as to the criteria for imprinting if we are to test the validity of this concept as applied to human development. What I propose to do is to start from considerations at the human level and continually to refer back to animal studies in which the concept has been developed. Since I will restrict myself to experimental studies this means referring mainly to work on the development and limitation of the following response in birds to a particular class of object.

Critique of Gray's paper on imprinting in humans

To begin with it will be useful to consider briefly what, as far as I know, is the first serious attempt to maintain that imprinting does operate in human infancy, in order to see to what extent we can agree with the conclusion reached. I refer to the article of P. H. Gray (1958) entitled 'Theory and Evidence of Imprinting in Human Infants'. Gray sets out to show 'that socialization, whereby an immutable bond is fostered between the young and its kind, is essentially the same in most or all species where a social complex is an attribute of survival'. He starts by distinguishing four of what he calls 'specific and distinct periods for social development', that is, in species not born at an advanced stage of neural and motor maturation. These are as follows: first the pre-learning period when the higher parts of the brain are immature, conditioning is not possible, and events that might otherwise be stressful have no demonstrable effect. Second, the imprinting period, and he defines imprinting as 'an innate disposition to learn the parent, or parent-surrogate'. Third, the period of infantile fear, and fourth the period of in-group learning, or learning of the non-parental individuals around the infant. After looking at some of the evidence for imprinting in birds, guinea-pigs, lambs and kittens he turns to humans. Pointing out that man is one of the few animals unable to walk immediately after the neonatal stage he says this uniqueness has forced the evolution of a different system of releasers and responses for imprinting. He proposes that the smiling response in human infants is the motor equivalent of the following response in animals below the higher primates. After summarizing the findings of Kaila and Spitz on the effectiveness of the human face-configuration as a releaser of smiling he makes the following statement: 'It is reasonable to place the critical period for imprinting in humans from about 6 weeks to about 6 months. It begins with the onset of learning ability, continues with the smiling response, and ends with the fear of strangers.' Finally he attempts to bear out his claim that 'the best evidence we have of imprinting in the human' is 'the incarceration of infants in institutions'; and he draws on the work of Bakwin, Levy, Brodbeck and Irwin, Spitz and Wolf, Durfee and Wolf, Lowery, and Goldfarb.

I have outlined the contents of Gray's paper sufficiently to show not only that it contains some interesting ideas, but also that it is both misleading and unwarranted in the conclusions that are reached. This is due to insufficient care both in the treatment of imprinting criteria and in the treatment of the data referred to. In the first place Gray's definition of imprinting is not in accordance with the view generally held by those who have studied imprinting in animals, which is that imprinting of following occurs naturally only in the period when the young animal is learning the characteristics of the species. Certainly this occurs through the infant learning the parent, but Gray's failure to qualify the phrase 'learning the parent' suggests that he regards imprinting as including, if not meaning, the process of learning the parent as an individual. Most writers on imprinting, however, are quite explicit that imprinting involves learning a class of object, and not the specific object itself. Gray in fact admits that his definition departs from the ethological definition in several respects, but to start with a departure of this sort without much evidence to support it would seem to confuse the issue right away.

Secondly, Gray gives no explanation for his proposal that the smiling response is the motor-equivalent of the following response. However, his summarizing of Spitz's work on smiling suggests that he bases the equivalence upon the assumption that both motor patterns begin to occur, and develop, in the period when what he calls 'learning the parent' also occurs, but before fear of strangers commences. Spitz inferred from his results that between the third and sixth months infants smile indiscriminately at the configuration of the face, but that they do not do so subsequently because they can then discriminate strangers, to whom they react with fear. It is with these considerations in mind that Gray reaches his belief that imprinting must take place in humans, and that the critical period must start when smiling begins to occur in response to the human face, and must end when the fear of strangers begins.

On the surface this may look quite an attractive argument, especially as the period when the infant smiles only at the configurational aspects of the face is a period when in fact he is responding to the face only as characteristic of the human species and not as distinctive of a single individual person. There are, however, a number of assumptions here which are in fact not warranted. First the fact that smiling and following responses in widely different organisms, birds and humans, should have something in common regarding the general nature of their releasing stimuli, while suggestive, certainly does not by itself warrant the assumption of the motor equivalence of their responses whatever that is. If by that is meant similarity either in developmental characteristics or in function, this can only be determined by direct comparison. Second, regarding the limits of the suggested critical period it has not always been found in animal

204

studies that this ends with a fear of strangers. The development of a fear response must not therefore be set up as a criterion for the termination of imprinting, even though it may in some species appear to operate in terminating it. In any case, even if the onset of fear of strangers is an important variable in human infancy from this point of view, it is not the case that it starts only at six months. As I shall show later, it usually starts much earlier, the actual time varying with conditions of caretaking. Third, regarding the suggested commencement of a critical period, it is not the case that six weeks marks the age of onset of learning ability in the human, even though it often marks the beginning of smiling at the human face. As we know, learning operates much earlier, especially through tactile, kinaesthetic and auditory sensory modes.

Finally, it is necessary to comment on Gray's attempt to demonstrate that the period described by him must be a critical one by the use of data on infants that have been in institutions over this period. He tries to maintain that there are critical consequences. First he refers to the behaviour of infants while in institutions over the period itself, emphasizing their developmental backwardness at six months. Second, to get at the issue of the irreversibility of what develops by six months he refers to studies in which infants have been in institutions during the period and tested later. While some of the evidence here is certainly suggestive it is by no means adequate to demonstrate critical consequences. This is partly because in several of the studies infants tested later had remained in their institution after the period in question, partly because the change to conditions of fostering after institutionalization presents additional problems which hamper the contrast between the effects of living in an institution and living in a family, and partly because the test criteria used are in many cases ambiguous.

I maintain therefore that the arguments put forward by Gray do not give grounds for concluding that imprinting operates in human infancy. The thesis, as handled by him, remains unproven. I suggest, however, that this is not because the thesis itself is implausible, but because it has been treated without sufficient attention to relevant details. It is my belief that there are in fact good grounds for maintaining the hypothesis that there is an early critical period in the development of the human infant's social responsiveness. But this hypothesis remains to be tested. My aim now will be to describe these grounds as a necessary prerequisite for any consideration of the problem of how crucial tests can be made.

Similarities between phenomena of early human social development and some of those associated with imprinting

The grounds for adopting a critical period hypothesis arise from both theoretical and experimental considerations. They consist of what appear to be a number of close formal similarities between, on the one hand, various characteristics of the development in the natural situation of an infant's social responsiveness to his mother and, on the other, some of the general types of change, described under the heading of imprinting, as the attachment of young birds becomes limited to a particular class of object. Now many different phenomena have been described as often characteristic of a critical period in which the following response becomes limited to a class of object. Not all of these, however, are to be regarded as criteria for imprinting as the term is usually used. The aim here is not to establish that certain similar phenomena at the human level are of the kind that would qualify as criteria for imprinting. It is merely to show that some phenomena often associated with imprinting are to be found at the human level. If this is so it would appear to warrant asking the question of whether or not the period when these phenomena occur is a critical one. This further issue would lead to inquiry on two main questions: first whether there is a special sensitivity as opposed to special opportunity for learning in certain directions during a brief limited period only, and second whether there are critical consequences of the events during the limited period. These consequences refer not necessarily to any specific later effects manifested in adulthood, but only to a relative stability of some sort of effect or other brought about during the period in question and not during any other period.

Keeping to the issue of the phenomena to be found at the human level, I would like to describe four similarities to the development of attachment behaviour in birds. The first concerns the relation between smiling and following which Gray rightly draws attention to but fails to explain in terms other than a broad similarity of the general type of natural releasing stimulation, namely the parent-figure. I would maintain that the two types of behaviour have in the early period not only rather closer similarities of causation but also similarity of function. The functional similarity arises from the fact, also noted by Gray, that in man the capacity for locomotion develops relatively later than in most other animals. More precisely, whereas many types of young bird are able to locomote and thereby keep in close contact with the parent during the period when learning of the class of the species is taking place, human infants cannot do so. Neither can they maintain contact with the mother by clinging in this period in the way that most other primates can, because they have nothing to cling to. The human infant therefore cannot maintain frequent close contact with his mother unaided by her. Since he cannot do this, and if such close relation between them in the early months is as important as it seems to be, then we might expect to find that either the initiative is left entirely to the mother, or that the infant has means of facilitating it as well. In fact he does seem to have such means, which have the effect of attracting her to himself. The crying response enables him to attract her from a distance, especially to meet his physiological needs, and thus contributes to ensuring the basic necessities for immediate survival. Beyond this, however, it seems to have marked limitation. The smiling response, I suggest, goes on from where it leaves off, and serves the infant's need for more than the basic minimum for physical survival. The characteristic effects of an infant's smiling on his mother show that it greatly fosters increased proximity between infant and mother as well as loving behaviour on the part of the mother. In this respect, therefore, the smiling response has a close similarity of function to the following response.

There is a second similarity between smiling and following. This is not only that they both develop in response strength in the period of learning of the species, but both seem to develop without any conventional reward such as food. Various suggestions have been made as to the nature of the reward operating in following, such as the act of following itself, or the maintaining of a close spatial relation with the object, or the achievement of anxiety reduction. This last suggestion by Moltz (1960) seems to me most plausible of all and is based on evidence that the first object which becomes familiar is followed because that object is associated with a state of low anxiety, whereas unfamiliar objects result in states of higher anxiety. In smiling the work of Brackbill (1958) shows clearly that response strength can be increased without reward of a physiological need-satisfying sort, but merely by a combination of smiling back at the infant, stroking and cooing at him, picking him up and holding him. One thing worth noting about this in view of Moltz's hypotheses about anxiety-reduction in following is that this sort of behaviour on the part of a mother is usually one of the most effective means of bringing about anxiety-reduction in infants.

A third similarity lies in the type of stimuli that release smiling and following. I refer here not just to the fact that both responses tend to become limited to the class of object first responded to, that is the species represented by the parent, but refer also to those stimulus properties of the parent that initially release these attachment responses. The following response is usually initially released by the first moving object seen. This object can be of almost any sort as long as it has the characteristic of motion, although there is evidence of species differences here: some objects may act as better cues than others of the same size. Since this release takes place even in animals kept isolated from birth (provided isolation does not continue for too long) it must be independent of previous social experience. The initial release by a moving object seems not to be essential since following has also been initially released by and limited to intermittent light and to repeated sound. In the natural situation both the motion and sound of the parent seem to operate in the initial release. Emphasis has been put, however, on the need for the initial releasing stimulus to be available over some period of time, and since motion and intermittent stimulation are conducive to fixation it may well be that following is initially released by those properties of stimulation that are first consistently fixated visually or auditorily and so first become familiar.

In the case of smiling the evidence indicates that as soon as early smiling movements come to be released by stimuli other than internal ones, these are usually auditory or tactile stimuli. But very soon visual stimuli having the properties of figure and motion become the most effective stimuli. In the natural situation these are usually represented by the eyes of a moving human being. Often auditory and tactile stimulation are necessary as well. Although the eyes are only part of an object it seems, from the results of Ahrens and others, that at the age when visual release first takes place the infant does not have the capacity for fixation of anything much larger. That the eyes are the first figural entity which is consistently perceived by the infant at the time when fixation first becomes possible is apparent from a number of facts of common experience. The mother is usually the only moving object in the infant's environment. When being cared for by her the head, especially the face, is the part of her which is within the infant's visual field most frequently. And of all the features of the face the eyes possess the greatest combination of those qualities which attract an infant's fixation: figure, small enough to be perceived with a minimum of multiple fixation, colour, albedo, movement, and light-reflection. It appears, therefore, that the eyes of the mother are the human equivalent of what in birds is the 'first moving object seen'.

This leads to a fourth similarity which concerns the sorts of factors that determine the limits of the rather brief period in which the learning of the species naturally occurs, and in which attachment behaviour develops to the type of object learned. Commencement of such learning seems to be conditional upon the achievement of the ability to fixate an object and not, as Gray suggests, the achievement of a capacity to learn at all. (A bird cannot possibly follow its parent unless it can keep it fixated, and unless it follows it is hardly likely to learn much about the parent's general characteristics.) What causes the termination of the imprinting period in following is less clear because of differences within, let alone between, species. Imprinting is, apparently, a process of supra-individual learning only, and is described as definitely not characteristic of the subsequent learning of the specific individual *per se* which enables discrimination from strangers even of the same species. As regards the time-limit for the possibility of supra-individual learning to take place, it has frequently been observed that the later an animal is first exposed to a releasing stimulus the greater is the tendency to flee from it instead of to follow it. This has led to the conclusion that the end of the critical period may be due to the development of fleeing, which is a response incompatible with following. Hinde (Hinde *et al.*, 1956) has pointed out that this would mean that the apparently striking nature of the limitation of the following response to a particular sort of object is due merely to the fact that the animal has become familiar with that object by the time the fleeing response develops. There is also evidence, however, that fear is not the only factor which may terminate the period. While in animals reared isolated until the fear response has developed fear inhibits following, in animals reared socially the following response to strange objects is lost earlier. This is due not so much to fear of the strange moving object but to the fact that if they follow it they lose their companions. As a result following is inhibited by other types of incompatible responses, namely persistent searching, distress and other forms of emotional behaviour which are elicited by isolation from their companions.

Now in human infants there are, as in birds, individual differences in the time when they begin not to respond socially to strangers. Considering responsiveness in terms of smiling the evidence I have brought forward (Ambrose, 1961) shows clearly that the age when infants begin to discriminate strangers, that is when supra-individual learning of the face of the human species stops, is much later for institution infants than for home, that is, family infants.

Furthermore, for both types of infant the discrimination of strangers seems to be associated with a type of response that interferes with smiling, probably fear, if not also curiosity, though family infants seem to show more of this than institution infants. I will report evidence for this later on. Such fear seems, however, not to be something that just clocks in through maturation (infants can show aversion responses from very much earlier on). Any fear seems to be caused specifically by the beginning discrimination of an unfamiliar face *per se*. Many infants soon overcome this (the fear habituates), and smile more at strangers again, although this smiling may then decline in strength through habituation to the stranger.

With regard to the actual timing of the period of supra-individual learning of the human face the evidence in the literature indicates that this starts at approximately the fifth week of life. Its termination, that is when the discrimination of strangers begins, is, according to the evidence of Bernstein and me, at approximately 12 weeks for family infants and approximately 18 weeks for institution infants. On the basis of the similarities with the development of the following response in birds that I have outlined, therefore, these would constitute the rough, obviously variable, limits for any critical period for the development of social responsiveness in human infants.

What then do we need to find out in order to determine whether or not this period of weeks is critical in human development? There are two aspects to the answer. One concerns the issue of whether it is a sensitive period for the development of social responsiveness

210

to the human species, and not just a period of special opportunity. This could only be settled if a group of infants was completely deprived of the opportunity to associate with a human being over the period in question and then first exposed to one at some later period. If social responsiveness did not then develop, this would be evidence in favour of the earlier period being a sensitive one. Since this is a practical impossibility for experimentation, and even congenitally blind babies whose sight is operatively restored much later would not settle the matter because of all the learning that proceeds through other sensory modes, this aspect of the question cannot be answered.

The other aspect concerns any critical consequences of events occurring during the period. Given the fact that all human infants must for survival inevitably associate with other human beings from birth onwards, we can still inquire into the nature and extent of the social responsiveness that develops during the period. In particular we may ask whether the development or non-development of responsiveness in that period has critical consequences. We need to know in fact whether the nature and amount of social responsiveness characteristic of an individual later on is related to that which develops during the early period in question, and especially when the environmental conditions operative during the period are altered once it is over.

Data on trends in social responsiveness and relationships between earlier and later levels

In order to facilitate thinking about this problem, and also about some of the other points I have raised, I would now like to present some data about changes that occur in the development of smiling over the first 10 months after birth. In doing so I am making the working assumption that the intensity of smiling that is characteristic of a particular infant at any given age may be taken as a rough index of his social responsiveness.

Many of you will be familiar with part of the data since it comes from the study carried out by Mrs Bernstein and myself which I have described previously (*op. cit.*). I shall now describe only that aspect of the study in which an attempt was made to measure the changes in response strength of smiling of eight infants, each at weekly intervals, over the period from six to thirty-six weeks of age. The aim in that study was to compare the changes in four of these infants who lived at home in the family setting with four who lived in an institution. (In the event only two of the institution infants could be seen for the whole period since two were adopted at 20 weeks.) The aim here is to make use of the data to bring out two main points: first, to show the trend of changes in smiling response-strength over what, according to my hypothesis, may be the critical period in question; second, to show there are good grounds for believing that the intensity of responsiveness achieved by the end of this period limits, if not determines, the level of responsiveness that is possible in the succeeding months. Regarding this latter point the data are not in any way conclusive; but they are not inconsistent with the critical consequences hypothesis and their consideration throws light on the problems of disproving this hypothesis.

The method of assessing the response-strength of smiling each week consisted of measuring the total number of seconds in which the infant smiled at a constant stimulus under standardized conditions. The stimulus was Mrs Bernstein's face and she presented this to the infant by standing beside his cot, motionless and expressionless, for a series of half-minute periods. These half-minute stimulus periods were each separated by a half-minute time-interval during which duration of smiling in each period was recorded. A series of stimulus presentations continued either until smiling waned completely or until twelve such presentations had been made, whichever occurred first. The measure thus obtained was referred to as smiling time per run of presentations.

The results show a number of distinct trends in smiling response-strength over different parts of the 30-week period studied, as well as individual differences in the timing and levels at which these occur. In order to describe these trends clearly it is necessary first to refer to two kinds of variation which, if not initially discounted, are apt to confuse the interpretation of the curve showing the trends for any particular infant. These variations are the effects of two accidental variables which inevitably intruded into the study. One arose from the fact that occasionally a week had to be missed out for such reasons as the infant's being away on holiday or not well enough to be tested. This gave rise to instances when the time-interval between tests was not one week but two weeks instead. This extended time-interval characteristically resulted in a temporary increase in smiling response-strength at the next test, although the percentage increase tended to become smaller with any subsequent extended time-interval. The other variable was that, towards the end of the age-period, some infants achieved sufficient postural control to enable them either to sit up or stand up in the cot, so that they would not always remain supine during a test. Such postural achievement had a characteristic effect of temporarily increasing smiling response-strength. In order that these two kinds of effects should be adequately discounted in discerning long-term trends of smiling response-strength, any values for smiling time obtained either for the week in which the accidental

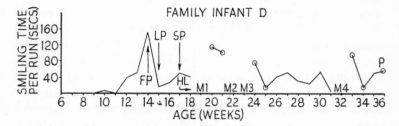

FIG. 20

Curve exemplifying typical trends and phases in the development of smiling in response to standard stimulation over the period six to thirty-six weeks of age, and showing the effects of accidental variables (see text). Measurement of response-strength obtained at weekly intervals from an infant girl living in a family setting

(FP = *first peak;* LP = *low point;* SP = *second peak;* HL = *habituation level;* M = *missed week;* P = *postural achievement;* ⊙ = *value discounted in assessment of habituation level*)

variable operated or for the two subsequent weeks were ignored. While this procedure considerably reduced the amount of data available for evaluation of trends in the case of some infants, the advantage of the increased validity of the data remaining was preferred.

I will now outline the trends, and in passing point out the operation of these special effects, as exemplified most clearly by the curve of an infant girl living in a family setting (Fig. 20), referred to in subsequent tables as Family Infant D. In this graph the values of smiling time per run are plotted against the age of testing. From six to eleven weeks there is virtually no smiling at the stimulus. Smiling then develops rapidly from twelve weeks to reach a peak at fourteen weeks, referred to as the 'first peak' (FP). The next week there is a precipitious fall in response-strength to a subsequent low point (LP), which is then followed by a gradual recovery to a second peak (SP) at seventeen weeks. From then onwards response-strength varies more or less from week to week, but it is striking that from the time of the second peak onwards variation occurs only within relatively narrow limits, the few large variations occurring only after a week had been missed. For example after the first and the fourth misses (M1 and M4) the extended time-interval is associated with a marked recovery of response-strength at the next week: it will be noted, however, that in the week following M4 there is a tendency in the direction of re-establishing the level reached before the extended time-interval (and this tendency operates after M1 as well). Now if the two runs after each extended time-interval are discounted (plots enclosed by a ring in Fig. 20) as well as the run where the infant began to sit up (P), it becomes apparent that the remaining values of response-strength show only restricted variability about a level which seems to be characteristic for the individual infant. This is referred to as the infant's habituation level (HL).

These trends and special effects are present, to greater or lesser degree, for all the infants studied. The ages at which the various stages occur for all four family infants and for all four institution infants are given in Table 10. The actual values of smiling time per run shown by each infant at these stages are given in Table 11. Among the family infants, by comparison with infant D already discussed, the other three infants have much lower absolute values, although the second peak is higher than the first peak for infants A and B; also most of infant A's stages occur earlier than for the other three. For the four institution infants, not only is the age of the first smiling run mostly later than for the family infants, but so also is the age of the first peak. There is one infant from each group which shows no second peak, their habituation level starting from the low point (LP).

I interpret these various trends, as exemplified in Fig. 20, the following way. For this infant in the period six to eleven weeks smiling has not developed sufficiently to be released by stationary visual stimulation alone, i.e. by the face without movement and perhaps without additional auditory and tactile stimulation. At twelve weeks the infant smiles at the investigator's face alone and the subsequent

214

TABLE 10

Age of occurrence of successive phases in the development of smiling in response to standard stimulation, over the period six to thirty-six weeks of age, in four family infants and four institution infants

(* = observations ceased due to unavailability of infant)

Group	Infant	Age of first smiling run	Age at first peak (FP)	Age at low point (LP)	Age at second peak (SP)	Age habituation level (HL) starts
Family	A	8	8	11	12	14
	B	6	11	12	19	23
	C	7	12	15	—	15
	D	10	14	15	17	17
Institu-tion	A	11	20	*	*	*
	B	9	16	18	20	23
	C	9	16	17	19	*
	D	9	16	19	—	19

big weekly increment in response-strength is due to the rapid development of smiling response-strength to the mother through the reinforcement she provides in natural everyday life. Up to the first peak at fourteen weeks this effect is generalized to the investigator whose face is not distinguished from that of the mother. Up to fourteen weeks, therefore, the increase in the response-strength of smiling is associated with supra-individual learning. The sudden sharp decline to a low point at fifteen weeks is due to the beginning of discrimination of the investigator's face from that of the mother. Supra-individual learning is at an end. The very precipitousness of the decline is one indicator that there seems to be massive inhibition by a newly interfering response here, probably fear elicited by the investigator's face newly discriminated as different from that of the mother, and unfamiliar. The subsequent gradual recovery of smiling up to the second peak suggests that that interfering response soon gets habituated, leaving smiling free to occur more strongly. At the second peak its strength is, however, different from that at the first

TABLE 11

Values of the response-strength of smiling (measured in terms of smiling time (seconds) per run of presentations) at successive phases in the development of smiling in response to standard stimulation over the period six to thirty-six weeks of age in four family infants and four institution infants

(* = measurements unobtainable due to unavailability of infant)

Group	Infant	First smiling run value	First peak value (FP)	Low point value (SP)	Second peak value (SP)	Habituation level			First recovery value
						Average value	N	σ	
Family	A	48·5	48·5	0·0	55·75	4·3	8	5·5	5·5
	B	6·5	68·25	3·75	94·5	0·3	5	0·67	88·75
	C	2·0	26·0	0·0	—	0·03	15	0·13	5·0
	D	2·0	157·0	16·75	49·25	39·6	9	17·5	121·25
Institution	A	1·5	124·75	*	*	*	*	*	*
	B	5·5	49·5	4·0	28·25	4·04	14	5·06	—
	C	8·0	121·75	18·25	111·5	*	*	*	*
	D	6·5	48·25	0·0	—	1·5	13	3·7	0·0

peak, in this case much less, which suggests that smiling has by then become habituated to a considerable extent. From then on, apart from the special effects mentioned, the relatively constant habituation level indicates that the infant has settled down to a fairly stable level of responsiveness to the investigator to whom he has become habituated. For two of the other infants (Family infants A and B), however, the level reached at the second peak is higher than that at the first peak. This indicates that, after habituation of the interfering (fear) response after the low point, the smiling response to the investigator has by no means yet become habituated and recovers to a level that is probably similar to that manifested in response to the mother. Habituation to the investigator soon sets in, however, although it may take a few weeks before it is fully achieved. Only then do these infants settle down at a relatively stable weekly level of responding, that is at the habituation level.

Now there are a number of interesting features connected with the part of the curve which for each infant I have called the habituation level. In the first place in this part of the curve the infant has settled down to a fairly stable level of social responsiveness to a person other than the mother. This person, the investigator, is a non-reinforcing stimulus for the infant's smiling, and yet some of the infants seem to have sufficient 'reserve' of responsiveness to go on smiling at him week after week. In these instances what is happening is that, from one week's test to the next, although smiling wanes completely by the end of one week's test, the infant after a further week's time-interval is still prepared to smile again at the investigator at the next test, and at about the same response-strength, even though smiling then wanes again. Also, incidentally, the longer the time-interval, as when a week is missed, the more the infant will smile at the next test. Other infants, on the other hand, show a habituation level that is virtually zero, and even with a longer time-interval between tests than the usual weekly one there is only a very small degree of recovery. This suggests that there is not much response-strength available to be recovered, and furthermore, since these infants show no recovery to a second peak after the low point, it may well be that any responsiveness that is available is seriously impeded by a continuing interfering response such as fear.

If now, taking note of the clearly differing habituation levels established by the various infants (Table 11) we look to see if these

217

are related to anything in the data that occurs before the levels are established, we come to a further feature. The data indicate a rather close correlation between the average value of each individual's habituation level, and the value of response-strength at the first peak. If the four family infants are ranked in terms of response-strength of smiling at first peak, and then ranked in terms of the average response-strength representing the habituation level, comparison of the two rankings (Table 12) shows that, while they are not exactly the same, they are close enough to suggest that a significantly positive correlation may well be obtained from a larger sample. Furthermore, a similar result occurs if the infants are ranked in terms of the value to which smiling response-strength recovers after the first extended time interval (Table 12, first recovery value). If this[1] ranking is compared with that for the first peak values we find the rankings are identical. In other words, it rather looks as if, for these infants, the level of responsiveness to people other than the mother that they settle down to is related to the level of responsiveness achieved earlier to the mother, and generalized to the investigator, in the period of supra-individual learning.

The same sort of indication comes from similar comparisons made for the two institution infants that could be observed up to 36 weeks of age: the one with the higher first peak also shows the higher habituation level. It is not possible to combine these results with those for the four family infants to give a total of six rankings, however, because the two groups are not living under comparable[2] conditions.

Now it may be thought that this relation could be due to the operation of other factors common to both earlier and later phases,

---

[1] Values after any subsequent extended time-intervals are not included because these are very likely to be influenced not just by the immediately preceding time-interval but also by the time since the time-interval before that one.

[2] In particular, during both supra-individual and individual learning periods, the institution infants have several different caretakers as opposed to the family infant's one caretaker. Therefore the contrast for the institution infant between the investigator and his several caretakers in the period after the first peak is likely to be rather different from that for the family infant between the investigator and his one caretaker. This factor appears likely to affect the habituation levels in the institution group. Hence the two groups are kept separate for ranking purposes.

TABLE 12

Rank orders of four family infants and two institution infants in respect of values for the response-strength of smiling in response to standard stimulation at successive phases of development over the period six to thirty-six weeks of age. Rankings of the four family infants also in respect of quality of the relation with mother as assessed by three judges (B, A, S)

(* = ranking not possible due to unavailability of infant)

Group	Infant	First smiling run value	First peak value (FP)	Low point value (LP)	Second peak value (SP)	Habituation level		First recovery value	Quality of relation with mother B. A. S.		
						Average value	σ		B	A	S
Family	A	1	3	3½	2	2	2	3	3	3	4
	B	2	2	2	1	3	3	2	2	2	1
	C	3½	4	3½	—	4	4	4	4	4	3
	D	3½	1	1	3	1	1	1	1	1	2
Institution	A	(4)	(1) 1	*	*	*		*			
	B	(3) 2	(3)	1	1	1		1			
	C	(1)	(2)	*	*	*		*			
	D	(2) 1	(4) 2	2	2	2		2			

such as a constitutionally determined readiness to smile, or to similarity of the environmental factors affecting smiling in both phases. As regards a constitutional factor, however, there are two kinds of evidence against this being the operative factor. One concerns the response-strength of smiling when it first occurs to the experimenter within the first few weeks of the experiment. If a constitutional factor does affect the response-strength of an infant's smiling, it is most likely to show up in individual differences in the response-strength of the earliest smiling of each infant. The values and rankings of this for all eight infants observed are shown in Tables 11 and 12 respectively. Comparison of this ranking with that for the level of smiling response-strength at the first peak shows a correlation that is virtually zero: the first peak response-strength is in no way related to an infant's initial response-strength at the beginning of the 36 week period of observation.

A second kind of evidence against there being a constitutional factor causing consistency in an infant's response-strength from one phase to another is the environmental factor of the quality and quantity of the mothering received by each infant, to which the level of responsiveness at first peak seems closely related. During the project an attempt was made to observe the nature of the relationship between infant and mother, observed before or after testing on each home visit. The clinical notes taken give some idea of the frequency of interaction, the extent to which the mother responded to the infant's signals, and the extent to which any response made by her was need-satisfying for the infant. From these notes it was possible to gain a rather general clinical picture of the quality of the mothering received by each of the infants. Bearing in mind the limitations of a comparison based on this sort of data, the family infants were ranked in terms of the impressions, gained by three judges, of the general quality of their mothering (Table 12). Comparison of the three rankings with the ranking for first peak values shows that, with two of the judges, the rankings were identical; but these judges were the most contaminated. The rankings of the third judge who was completely uncontaminated matched less well, but still the top two and the bottom two in the ranking match up. These results do at least suggest, then, that first peak responsiveness is not primarily constitutionally determined but is to be understood rather in terms of the extent to which the infant's mother reinforces his smiling by her characteristic responsiveness to him. Brackbill's evidence also indicates the dominant role of learning in the development of smiling response-strength.

Now the evidence presented so far indicates the fact of marked individual differences in the levels of smiling response-strength at various phases, as well as individual consistencies in the levels at these different phases. It does not, however, enable us to say that the later level of responsiveness is a critical consequence of the establishment of a given level of responsiveness in an earlier period. After all each infant had broadly the same environmental conditions in the later period as in the earlier one. Even if for some reason responsiveness could not be developed in the earlier period, might it not just as well have developed in the normal way in the later period? This crucial issue can, of course, only be settled by comparison of response-strength as between earlier and later periods in cases where there is a marked change in conditions of maternal care from the first to the second period.

Unfortunately (or fortunately) cases of this kind are hard to come by. Only one infant observed by Mrs Bernstein failed to develop much smiling in the early period up to 12 weeks of age. This infant's mother suffered severe difficulties in mothering him during the first three months, but subsequently surmounted some of these and became much more effective as a mother. Nevertheless not only did this infant not develop much smiling in the later period, but in the test situation manifested totally atypical behaviour in general. Most infants during both earlier and later test-periods show a certain amount of other behaviour such as thumb-sucking, general motility, vocalization, occasional rocking, and several other sorts of behaviour. This infant, however, was conspicuous for the frequency and intensity of his thumb-sucking, rocking, squirming and turning away from the investigator. There was usually intense general motility with arching of the back up from the mattress and falling back with a loud thud. There was much vocalization with a sort of desperate urgent note in it, and shrieking and crying. It is quite possible that this disturbed behaviour associated with late-developing smiling is due to the failure to develop much social responsiveness in the earlier period. In this instance, however, there were complicating factors which vitiate such an inference, perhaps even neurological abnormalities.

Taking all the sorts of evidence I have presented, as a whole it does appear to give further grounds for seriously asking the crucial question of whether or not the social responsiveness developed to the mother during the supra-individual learning period critically affects the degree of social responsiveness that can be directed to other people in later periods. To put the question rather more clinically: Is a child's capacity to form and maintain human relationships, and the quality of the relationships he establishes, rooted in the nature of the relationship he is able to establish with his mother in the first three months or so of life? Does the infant's picture of his mother that he gradually builds up in the first three months, his first picture of a human being, form the prototype of the picture he has of all later individuals of the same species? Even if the answer is positive this does not at all imply that later vicissitudes such as separation from the mother, or change to other caretakers, cannot also have far-reaching effects on the quality of subsequent relationships. What it would imply is that the nature of the response to later vicissitudes is likely to be markedly affected by the predisposition set up in the early period in question.

Rationale

You may well ask if there is any sort of rationale which might at all justify the posing of this sort of question. Certainly Thorpe's (1956) rationale for a critical period in the organization of the following response does not appear relevant. He has argued, with reference to an IRM that releases the following response, that its lack of selectivity renders the social behaviour of the animal potentially susceptible to control by almost any relatively large object having the quality of motion. Obviously this condition, if continued, is biologically not adaptive so that early in ontogeny the animal must acquire a preference for a particular class of object towards which to direct its social behaviour. But time is short and what the animal has to learn is extremely urgent and important for its whole future. Hence imprinting is restricted to a rather brief critical period.

This conception of imprinting as a process that functions to increase the specificity of a hypothetical releasing mechanism does not provide any basis for a rationale for a critical period in the organization of the human infant's social responsiveness. There is no sort of evidence to which it can be related at all. What I have to suggest as a rationale stems from Moltz's interpretation of the results of imprinting experiments. He explains these in terms of anxiety-reduction: following of the first object that becomes familiar occurs because of its effect in bringing about anxiety-reduction in the young animal.

In the human infant, if we assume that the pre-eminent manifestation of anxiety or fear in the early months is crying, we know that this is usually elicited by intense stimulation, external or internal, such as a loud noise, hunger, or pain; also by stimulation that is unfamiliar. In the early weeks of life anxiety from such causes is frequently elicited in everyday life. Now the infant, independently, can do nothing about reducing this anxiety: for this he is entirely dependent upon actions by his mother, such as feeding, picking up and holding, rocking, cooing, etc. etc. As we know, some mothers consistently succeed by their actions in bringing about anxiety-reduction, others only sometimes, some hardly at all. Indeed some mothers seem to elicit more anxiety than they reduce.

Now in the period of supra-individual learning up to about three to four months, the infant is gradually piecing together and building up his picture of what a human being is like. He learns this from the first member of the human species he interacts with, namely his mother. When he learns the characteristics of the species via her, one of the things he learns is what the human face and clothed body are like; also the voice, touch, smell of the human being. All these gross physical characteristics we might call morphological ones. It is the learning of these that has been emphasized in animal imprinting studies. The fact is, however, that the human mother confronts the baby with more than these. She also has characteristics of behaviour which she manifests to the infant as she cares for him. Furthermore, all the variety of behaviour she carries out have effects in satisfying his physiological needs to varying extents, and reducing anxiety, or again increasing it. That is, the infant also learns from the nature of his mother's responsiveness what sort of behaviour he can expect from a human being. Depending on what his mother is like, his picture of a human being may turn out to be anything between two extremes. At one extreme it may be a loving, or need-satisfying, anxiety-reducing benign person, who he can depend on, enjoy, love, respond to positively. At the other extreme it may be a hating, rejecting, poor need-satisfier, who perhaps frequently elicits anxiety and lets him in for long periods of frustration, and who the infant cannot depend on, often hates, responds to negatively and above all with anxiety. Every infant must in fact have some degree of each sort of perception of his mother. Where infants vary will be in the balance between the amount of good and bad aspects built up. In other words some infants' picture of a human being will be one which elicits in them much more anxiety than in others.

Now the time comes at three to four months or earlier when the infant begins to learn that there are some human beings who are rather different from the one he's been getting used to and that there must be more than one human being around. Nevertheless on the principle of generalization to similar stimuli, in this case to other members of the same class or species as the mother, he will transfer his perception of and responsiveness to his mother to these new people. Once he's got over their immediate unfamiliarity he will respond to them with just that combination of social responsiveness and anxiety he has learned in relation to his mother.

But since they are different from the mother in fact, especially in their behaviour, will he not learn a different picture of them and respond to them differently? My point is that this will depend upon the amount of anxiety he transfers to them in the first place. If this is high or excessive the aversive tendency to withdraw will exceed any tendency to approach or socially respond and the expression of this tendency will therefore be inhibited and prevented. But if this happens it means that the infant withdraws from the learning situation: he has no opportunity to learn that the new person *is* any different from his mother. Consequently he will go on responding as if it were his mother, that is with only very restricted social responsiveness and heaps of anxiety. If, on the other hand, the infant's relation with his mother has not become loaded with anxiety, the level of anxiety transferred to a new person will be much less. It will not therefore be such as to prevent positive social responsiveness and continued interaction with the person, in which the infant can learn the differences from the mother and adapt appropriately.

What I am suggesting, then, is that the events of the supra-individual learning period may quite possibly have critical consequences for the organization of the infant's social responsiveness, and perhaps also for his capacity to establish and maintain adaptive human relationships in general. One can, of course, conceive of a number of possible mechanisms by which such critical consequences might take effect. I have outlined only one, however, because this is the one I am most immediately interested to explore further.

Acknowledgements

The Research was undertaken as part of the work of the Tavistock Child Development Research Unit, which is supported by the National Health Service and by grants from the Josiah Macy Junior Foundation, the Foundations' Fund for Research in Psychiatry and the Ford Foundation, to all of which our thanks are due. We also wish to express our gratitude to the London County Council and the Thomas Coram Foundation for permission to work in the Nurseries under their jurisdiction.

The Nature of Imprinting

R. A. HINDE

Yesterday Ambrose asked 'Is this imprinting or isn't it?' To consider this question for learning in any particular context, one must go back to Lorenz's four criteria of imprinting. These were formulated as a result of his studies of the development of the young-parent relationship in nidifugous birds, and on this basis he supposed that imprinting was a special form of learning quite different from 'associative' learning. The criteria were that the learning is irreversible, that it takes place in a limited sensitive period, that it is supra-individual learning, and that it influences patterns of behaviour which have not yet developed in the organism's repertoire.

Now some workers have taken the first two of these, which refer to the initial learning itself, as the definitive characteristics of imprinting, while others have laid the emphasis on the last two, which refer to the consequences of the learning in later life. Let us consider the latter first. It is now well established that birds reared by foster parents of another species may subsequently direct their sexual behaviour towards individuals of their foster parents' species. As yet, however, it is not clear at what age the choice of the sex partner was determined, for the experiences during the latter part of the juvenile period and adolescence have not been controlled. Thus as yet little is known about the extent to which 'imprinting', as it is usually studied in the context of the following response of the newly hatched bird, affects later sexual behaviour. In any case the aberrant sexual behaviour may be a consequence of the early learning, but is hardly a characteristic. The observation that imprinting involves supra-individual learning may be true if we are concerned solely with the later consequences of the learning, for in so far as early learning does affect later sexual behaviour, imprinted birds tend to pair with individuals which resemble their mothers or foster mothers and not

227

with their mothers themselves. But the initial learning of the characteristics of the parent is not supra-individual – the young bird learns the individual's characteristics. Indeed it has to, because it gets into trouble if it tries to follow another mother.

If we are concerned with the peculiarity of the learning process itself, it is the first two of Lorenz's characteristics which we must consider. As far as the irreversibility goes, this was clearly very much over-estimated in the early reports of imprinting in birds, for it certainly can be reversed in certain circumstances. In the following response of nidifugous birds the question of a sensitive period is a relative one. It isn't a matter, as the early reports implied, of a period during which learning can occur, surrounded by periods during which it can't, but rather of a gradual change in the probability that learning will occur. Even in some of the more recent reports, the sharpness of the limits to the sensitive period have been very much over-emphasized by the use of misleading criteria: if one uses measures like the proportion of birds which followed a model, you get very much sharper curves than if you take more detailed measures into account.

Now it is a legitimate working assumption that all learning is more likely to occur at some stages in the life cycle than it is at others: imprinting is merely a particularly clear cut case. The question in each particular case is thus: what limits the period during which learning is more probable? Ambrose mentioned some of the possibilities for the limiting factors in the case of the following response of nidifugous birds, and it is clear that even amongst birds, different factors may operate in different species.

In parenthesis, I would make two points about sensitive periods. From what Ambrose has said about Gray's paper it sounded as though he was thinking in terms of *a* critical period for learning in the species, whereas it is clear that what we are usually dealing with are sensitive periods for particular responses, each response having its own particular sensitive period. Furthermore, in discussions of sensitive periods we must distinguish two different categories. In the first, one is dealing with a sensitive period for learning X which is critical for the subsequent performance of X. This is the case with most studies of the following response in birds, where the bird is taught to follow a model, and the thing that is subsequently tested later is following the model. In the second case there is a sensitive

228

period for learning X which is critical for the later performance of Y. In the studies of the smiling response, it is this latter type of thing which is perhaps the more interesting.

It seems, then, that on the basis of Lorenz's four criteria, imprinting is not a special type of learning. It is therefore not useful to ask whether imprinting occurs in mammals or not, or whether the learning which accompanies smiling is or is not imprinting. You can of course ask questions like 'Do mammals learn to follow strange objects?' and the answer for some mammals is certainly 'Yes'. One could ask 'Does this have to occur within a certain sensitive period?' and the answer again is 'Yes'. 'Does it influence later sexual behaviour?'– I don't think anybody knows, but it is possible. One can also ask whether learning occurring in other contexts shares characteristics with classical imprinting, but I think it is not very useful to ask whether it is imprinting or not. Of course this doesn't mean that the concept of imprinting isn't useful. One point is that birds and mammals are faced with many of the same problems in their ontogeny and we can expect them to show the same sorts of characteristics of behaviour as a result of convergence produced by natural selection. From a functional viewpoint, it is necessary that the learning shown in the two cases should show many characteristics in common. Seeing the problems in the one case may highlight the problems in the other case, but it won't provide the answers. We have got to analyse each case in detail in its own right. If we are interested in the mechanisms underlying behaviour, the superficial comparisons one can make between mammals and birds are nothing more than pointers for analysis.

At the same time we must not forget about the consequences of the learning, and its function in the life of the organism. Indeed there is a danger of the core of the problem being missed if we concentrate solely on the learning itself. As it happens in nature, the result of the imprinting process is that the young bird learns to recognize its mother as an individual, and a number of discrete responses made by the young animal to its mother become integrated on to one object. Now this raises a point about the development of behaviour in general and of mother-infant interaction in particular. By and large, and making no assumptions about the neural mechanisms involved, it is often useful to think of behaviour as being hierarchically structured. If you think of, say, feeding and changing and cuddling a baby, all these form part of maternal care and each of them in their turn depends on a number of patterns of movement. Now without getting involved in an innate/learning controversy, we can ask just what is present at the beginning of each stage of development. Here I think the answers are rather different for the mother and for the baby. You can conceptualize her behaviour in terms of the higher levels of integration in the hierarchy being present from the start – she wants to look after the baby, but the lower levels and the particular patterns of movement with which she will do so have to be acquired. With the baby, on the other hand, particular patterns of movement are present, and they may be already wired up to the stimuli which switch them on and off, but it's the higher levels of integration which are lacking. In other words, in those early months of the baby's life the goals for the higher levels of hierarchical integration are not yet present. Of course this distinction I have drawn between the development of the mother's behaviour and that of the baby's is much too crude, but it may provide a useful way of thinking about the role of smiling. One's got to think not only of the immediate responses which smiling evokes from the mother but also of the way in which it influences the goals at a higher level of integration.

Discussion following paper by Dr Ambrose and contribution from Dr Hinde

BOWLBY *At various times we have talked about several concepts which may or may not be related to each other – attachment, imprinting, and critical or sensitive periods. (I myself prefer the term 'sensitive period', since it does not carry an all-or-nothing implication.) One of our problems is: are we extending the scope of these concepts so much that they are losing their value?*

HINDE *In the case of imprinting, many people have stretched the concept so that it covers all those kinds of learning which have some resemblance to 'classical' imprinting. For instance Thorpe (1961) has done this; and I think it has value in that it draws attention to the way in which diverse examples of learning are similar from a func-*

tional point of view; but it should not lead one to believe that they rely on similar mechanisms.

AMBROSE *What would you say are the advantages if any in saying that some human behaviour is imprinted?*

HINDE *It may be useful to point out that a baby's smile and a gosling's following response have similar functions, but it is a mistake to label the learning involved in the two cases 'imprinting' if this carries an implication that they have special characteristics in common which distinguish them from other examples of learning.*

FOSS *If we could confine ourselves to the following response, it seems to me to have some characteristics – and perhaps smiling has too – which are unusual. The response is instinctive, not learnt. It is the object to be followed which is learnt. The eliciting stimulus and the reinforcing stimulus are identical. Also a discriminated preference for one object is developed in the absence of any conventional reinforcers.*

HINDE *I don't find it useful to distinguish between instinctive and learned in this way; and it's certainly possible to get a rat to press a lever in a Skinner box for reinforcers which are not conventional. I cannot see that you have made a fundamental distinction between the learning processes involved here and those involved in, say, operant conditioning.*

HARLOW *Except that the behaviour is elicited, not emitted. In a Skinner box, you have a terrible time getting the response you want.*

FOSS *If a moth flies constantly to one particular flame, you would not expect it to cease flying to other flames.*

GEWIRTZ *In that case either the flame is not providing reinforcement or the moth is not discriminating; but this seems not to be the right model, for the gosling pretty soon develops or acquires aversive responses for other moving objects, and this helps on the discrimination.*

FOSS *But if Jaynes (1957) is to be believed, this discrimination learning does not relate in a simple way to the strength of fleeing; and from the discussion following Mary Ainsworth's paper, there seems to be some agreement that a child discriminates the mother's face long before fear of strangers has developed.*

HINDE *I don't think that rules out the possibility that some aversive responses to the followed object have become habituated.*

GEWIRTZ *But even that assumption would not be necessary. The*

231

object followed provides discriminative stimuli signalling that the occasion is set for reinforcement, conventional or other.

BOWLBY *It seems to me that the term imprinting is not very valuable to us, but 'sensitive period' may well be. It seems to me that it is purely an empirical matter whether an animal has a sensitive period for a certain kind of learning. What is in principle more difficult is to decide what factors limit that period. Can I ask if there is evidence for sensitive periods in mammals?*

AMBROSE *To give one example, there are the studies by Scott (1950) where puppies were isolated during a so-called critical period, and their later social responsiveness was affected.*

ROWELL *But the whole point about puppies is that they can form these tremendous attachments to humans and yet lead what look like normal social lives with dogs, and breed satisfactorily. The isolation studies of Scott and others are not, I think, evidence for or against imprinting.*

RHEINGOLD *Some time ago the Social Science Research Council called a conference of child and comparative psychologists (Palmer, 1962). Its purpose was to discuss data from animal experiments which might bear on the concept of critical periods and to examine the implications of these data for child research. The members of the conference found it difficult to agree on a definition of critical periods.*

HINDE *I can see that sensitive period is a quite useful descriptive term. For instance, in the learning of languages, it is probably useless to start too early, and it certainly becomes more difficult if one learns too late. So in a sense there is a sensitive period but using the term does not explain the phenomenon.*

BOWLBY *When one starts talking about sensitive period, one has to ask with regard to what response the period is sensitive. For instance, is it smiling, or some subsequent social response?*

AMBROSE *Yes. If there is a sensitive period for the learning of X, is it sensitive for the subsequent performance of X or for something else, Y? I have been thinking of a sensitive period for smiling as being sensitive, not so much for later smiling in particular as for the later development of social responsiveness. Although I have talked almost exclusively about smiling, I regard this behaviour in the early months of life as an index of the baby's social responsiveness, which includes other behaviour as well. A baby's smile may be accompanied by all kinds of bodily movements and sounds which look like attempts to form social relationships. So perhaps my thesis is more acceptable if we think of the period as being sensitive for the learning of these responses too.*

The Concepts of Imprinting and Critical Period from a Psycho-analytic Viewpoint

J. D. SUTHERLAND

Ambrose raised the question of what connection there can be between the kind of phenomena we have been describing under terms like 'imprinting' and 'critical phase' and what one sees in the adult patient. The familiar justification for a connection is somewhat as follows. A wide range of psychodynamic psychotherapists (i.e. holding different theoretical views) would agree that the essence of most psychoneurotic difficulties is a conflict between incompatible patterns in relationships. Typically, and if a very generalized statement is allowed for, the adult patient wants to make a good mature heterosexual relationship as a means of satisfying sexual and parental needs but is unable to do so. (I have mentioned only the close heterosexual relationship but the same is true of other relationships including non-personal relationships, e.g. the relationship of the individual to his work.) On the one hand, inhibiting forces may prevent him starting such a relationship or, on the other, forces begin to intrude into one that he was able to establish and sooner or later destroy it. Further, these forces that are incompatible with the 'good' relationship can usually be recognized as belonging, and directly related, to a phase of childhood, often to very early phases. For example, clinical work repeatedly exposes the incompatible aims and patterns in relationships as wishes to be treated in various ways as the baby or to treat others as though they were re-incarnations of parents as the individual felt about the latter at various phases of his childhood.

This kind of behaviour appears to imply processes which the clinician considers must give a perspective to the studies of what goes on in early development. First, certain frustration experiences with his objects seem to set up sub-systems in the person which, though their aims may be unrecognized, remain as active systems constantly seeking expression despite the pressure of other, more central, systems which try to inhibit them. Second, these sub-systems are relatively little influenced by subsequent training. (They constitute in fact the so-called 'fixations'.) There is, however, a curious feature of their activity in that, although the relationships they seek are so inappropriate to the adult, they can influence in a profound way all the processes of the central part of the person, his perception of, his thinking and feeling about, and his actions towards the world around him. Thus a common finding in clinical work with disturbed marriages is to find that one or other partner, after a period in which the relationship has been experienced by both as good, will begin to 'look for' behaviour to support a growing 'conviction' about the other as unsatisfactory in some way. It is also a not inaccurate description to put it that he or she 'engineers' situations to make the other behave in a 'bad' way.

What the link is between this behaviour and some of the phenomena we have been considering I find very hard to see at this stage. I certainly feel a need to envisage the rapid building up of much more complex processes than some of the molecular ones we have been hearing about. Hinde's statement to this effect and Harlow's reference to affectional responses came nearer to the behaviour I have to be concerned with. This latter aspect interested me particularly. As you know, a characteristic of these split-off systems which have got left out of the main stream of development is the amount of affect attached to them (the first feature of them that Freud noted). When you can expose something of their nature to the individual there is commonly a considerable affective discharge. This made me want to ask whether or not in these learning phases and sensitive periods associated with fixation it is not only the time of their occurrence that matters. The time factor is obviously important, but are there certain properties or certain states of the organism present for what we call 'fixation' or 'imprinting' to occur. If there were, these states would have to be related to fairly complex organizations because I do not think one can talk about affects unless one is dealing with a high level of organization. Another aspect of the psychoneurotic patient, as contrasted with the monkeys referred to this morning, is that he has a model of what he wants. He knows what he wants presumably because most babies, unlike Harlow's surrogate babies, have enough experience of

236

what good mothering is to build in them images of what they want. These may be idealized or fantasy images, but they do embody a pattern which determines what the individual wants.

Another interesting feature about this trying to undo the frustrated relationship of the past that comes into the psychoneurotic behaviour is the following. It is a phenomenon that also emerges particularly clearly in working with disturbed marriages. Individual A marries a young woman B and things go quite well. Now, suppose A has a frustrated mothering need. It is usual too for there to be some angry feeling about these frustrated needs. A, however, does not tend to take that frustration and all the negative feelings about it to somebody else. Instead, it seems to be most important for him to work out the frustration on the person who matters to him. Often one thinks why could not some of these husbands get rid of their rage elsewhere – 'kick the cat' or something similar – but it must be on the wife. This frustration is made to reappear in the good relationship as though that is where it has to be undone – perhaps because that is where it started.

We have learned too, I think, in psychoneurosis that some of the relatively molecular symptom expressions, e.g. a fetish or a phobia, really belong to wider frustrations and it is only when these wider frustrations are experienced that changes occur in the symptom. In short, therefore, it did seem to me that there was plenty of evidence in the work with neurotic patients to show that something 'fixates' and survives from earlier phases; but its content and its manifestations need the postulation of much higher order variables than the kind of molecular behaviour we were considering.

Discussion following Dr Sutherland's contribution

HINDE *I didn't follow when you said categorically that your humans had images or something and that the surrogate babies didn't have images.*

SUTHERLAND *I don't think I'm saying that monkeys can't have an image. All I'm saying is that the particular monkeys brought up on a wire mother or in a wire cage wouldn't have an image of a good mother because they have never known one.*

HINDE *I find it terribly difficult to know whether one is playing with words when one talks about this, but in so far as these young monkeys struggle and strive to gain a certain situation in which they are being mothered correctly, and in so far as that struggling and striving ceases when they gain that situation, they must have some ability to recognize that situation.*

AINSWORTH *To know what they want.*

HINDE *In that sense they have an image of what a mother is. In the same sort of way a bird goes on building a nest until it's built one even if it's never seen one before and it stops building when it has built one, and in that sense it is able to recognize what a nest is like.*

SUTHERLAND *I grant that point. I think the neurotic patient would be comparable to the monkey that had some days on the towel and some days with a real mother – a mixture of experience.*

BOWLBY *The infant monkeys, the children of the unmothered-mothers, have never had any experience of a good mother, because these unmothered-mothers are terribly bad mothers. None the less, they struggle and they strive and do all sorts of things until the mother gets better at it and provides them with more of what they are after, even though they themselves have had no experience of it previously. That's really the crux of it, isn't it? I think there's no doubt that human infants who have had for, say, a couple of years or more a good relationship to a mother figure, and then lose it, show many signs that they have some sort of image of what they are after. Certainly that's true in plenty of examples when loss occurred at three, four or five years. It doesn't mean to say that this obtains in all humans who are seeking, as we would call it, a mother figure. Some do have images, perhaps distorted and idealized, but others, I think, don't. I can think of certain sorts of children in whom I've never seen any sign of an image. Some of these affectionless children who have lost a mother very early on seem singularly unalive to what it is they are after, even though we believe we know what it is.*

SUTHERLAND *There's certainly a range of awareness of images. For instance, if you take schizophrenics, it's very doubtful you could get an account of an image of what they wanted from many schizophrenics, but the striking thing about insulin treatment was not so much that it had any biochemical effect but that these people had the extraordinary experience of being mothered. They literally do come out of comas mouthing and sucking and attempting to be held and*

238

patted by the nurse, so they look as if they have some idea of what it is to be mothered.

BOWLBY *One difficulty is that as clinicians we are always inclined to attribute to our patients images and expectations, if not conscious at least unconscious, because that's an easy way for us to conceptualize our patients' behaviour. But it doesn't mean to say they have got them.*

HINDE *Sutherland implied that when something goes wrong it's because a 'higher order thing' becomes split off; but might it not be that in the development of some children this higher order thing has never developed at all, because all the smiling responses and other social interactions have been missing?*

BOWLBY *There's good reason to think you get both sorts of case. You may get a failure to develop a 'higher order thing' – and some of these affectionless psychopaths might conform to that pattern. On the other hand there are patients who at the age of three, four or five have lost a significant figure and who have then gone into a phase of pathological mourning, which may continue for many decades. The 'higher order thing' has developed and then become split off.*

References

AHRENS, R. (1954) 'Beitrag zur Entwicklung der Physiognomie und Mimikerkennens'. *Zeit für exp. und ang. Psychol.*, **2** (3), 414–54; and **2** (4), 599–633.

AMBROSE, J. A. (1961) 'The development of the smiling response in early infancy'. In B. M. Foss (Ed.) *Determinants of Infant Behaviour.* London: Methuen.

ARSENIAN, J. M. (1943) 'Young children in an insecure situation'. *J. abn. soc. Psychol*, **38**, 225–49.

BALDWIN, A. L., KALHORN, J., and BREESE, F. H. (1949) 'The appraisal of parent behaviour'. *Psychol. Monogr.*, **63**, No. 299.

BERGMAN, P., and ESCALONA, S. K. (1949) 'Unusual sensitivities in very young children'. *Psychoan. study of the child*, **3, 4.**

BERLYNE, D. E. (1960) *Conflict, Arousal and Curiosity.* New York: McGraw Hill.

BOWLBY, J. (1958) 'The nature of the child's tie to his mother'. *Int. J. Psycho-Anal.*, **39**, 350–73.

BRACKBILL, Y. (1958) 'Extinction of the smiling response in infants as a function of reinforcement schedule'. *Child Devel.*, **29**, 115–24.

CRAMOND, W. A. (1954) 'Psychological aspects of uterine dysfunction'. *Lancet*, 1241–5.

DARWIN, C. (1872) *The Expression of the Emotions in Man and Animals.* London.

DAVIDS, A., DEVAULT, S., and TALMADGE, M. (1961) 'Psychological study of emotional factors in pregnancy: a preliminary report'. *Psychosomat Med.*, **23**, 93–103.

DIJKSTRA, J. (1960) 'De prognostische betekenis van neurologische afwijkingen bij pasgeboren kinderen' unpublished thesis, Groningen.

ERIKSON, E. H. (1950) *Childhood and Society.* New York: Norton.

ESCALONA, S. K. (1962) 'The study of individual differences and the problem of state'. *J. Am. Acad. Child Psychiatry*, **1**, 11–37.

GÉBER, M. (1956) 'Développement psycho-moteur de l'enfant Africain'. *Courrier*, **6**, 17–29.

GÉBER, M. (1960) 'Problèmes posé par le développement du jeune enfant Africain en fonction de son milieu social'. *Le travail Humain*, **23**, 97–111.

GOUGH, D. (1962) 'The visual behaviour of infants in the first few weeks of life'. *Proc. Roy. Soc. Med.*, **55**, 308–10.

GRAY, P. H. (1958) 'Theory and evidence of imprinting in human infants'. *J. Psychol.*, **46**, 155–66.

HANDLIN, O. (1959) *Boston's Immigrants*. Cambridge, Mass.: Belknap Press, Harvard.

HARLOW, H. F. (1960) 'Primary affectional patterns in primates'. *Amer. J. Orthopsychiatr.*, **30**, 676–84.

HARLOW, H. F., and ZIMMERMANN, R. R. (1959) 'Affectional responses in the infant monkey'. *Science*, **130**, 421–32.

HEBB, D. O. (1955) 'The mammal and his environment'. *Amer. J. Psychiatr.*, **11**, 826–31.

HINDE, R. A., THORPE, W. H., and VINCE, M. A. (1956) 'The following response of young moorhens and coots'. *Behaviour*, **9**, 214–42.

HINDE, R. A., and ROWELL, T. E. (1962) 'Communication by postures and facial expression in the rhesus monkey (*Macaca mulatta*)'. *Proc. Zool. Soc.*, **138**, 1–21.

JAYNES, J. (1957) 'Imprinting: the interaction of learned and innate behaviour: II. The critical period'. *J. comp. physiol. Psychol.*, **50**, 6–10.

JENSEN, G. D., and TOLMAN, C. W. (1962) 'Mother–infant relationship in the monkey, *Macaca nemestrina*: the effect of brief separation and mother–infant specificity'. *J. comp. physiol. Psychol.*, **55**, 131–6.

LEVY, D. M. (1960) 'The infant's earliest memory of inoculation: A contribution to public health procedures'. *J. genet. Psychol.*, **96**, 3–46.

LORENZ, K. (1935) 'Companionship in bird life', pp. 83–128 in C. H. Schiller (Ed.) *Instinctive Behaviour*. London: Methuen.

MEAD, M. (1954) 'Some theoretical considerations on the problem of mother-child separation'. *Amer. J. Orthopsychiatr.*, **24**, 471–83.

MEAD, M. (1961) 'A cultural anthropological critique of *Maternal care and mental health*'. W.H.O.

MIDDLEMORE, M. P. (1941) *The Nursing Couple*. London: Cassell.

MOLTZ, H. (1960) 'Imprinting: empirical basis and theoretical significance'. *Psychol. Bull.*, **57**, 291–314.

References

PALMER, F. H. (1962) 'Critical periods of development: report of a conference'. Social Science Research Council *Items*, **15**, 13–18.

PIAGET, J. (1955) *The Child's Construction of Reality*. London: Routledge and Kegan Paul.

PRECHTL, H. F. R. (1953) 'Die Entwicklung der frühkindlichen Motorik'. I. Die Nahrungsaufnahme. 16-mm Filme Institut für den wissenschaftlichen Film Göttingen.

PRECHTL, H. F. R. (1961) 'The long term value of the neurological examination of the newborn infant'. *Little Club Clinics in Developmental Medicine*, No. 2, 69–74.

PRECHTL, H. F. R. (1962) In J. Money (Ed.) *Reading Disability Progress and Research Needs in Dyslexia*. Johns Hopkins.

PRECHTL, H. F. R., and STEMMER, C. J. (1959) 'Ein choreatiformes Syndrom bei Kindern'. *Wiener med. Wschr.*, **109**, 461–3.

PRECHTL, H. F. R., and STEMMER, C. J. (1962) 'A choreiform syndrome in children'. *Child Neur. Devel. Med.*, No. 4.

RHEINGOLD, H., (1961) 'The effect of environmental stimulation upon social and exploratory behaviour in the human infant'. In B. M. Foss (Ed.) *Determinants of Infant Behaviour*. London: Methuen.

RHEINGOLD, H. L., STANLEY, W. C., and COOLEY, J. A. (1962) 'Method for studying exploratory behaviour in infants'. *Science*, **136**, 1054–5.

ROSE, J. A. (1961) 'The prevention of mothering breakdown associated with physical abnormalities in the infant'. In G. Caplan (Ed.) *Prevention of Mental Disorders in Children*. New York: Basic Books.

ROWELL, T. E., and HINDE, R. A. (1962) 'Vocal communication by the Rhesus monkey'. *Proc. Zool. Soc.*, **138**, 279–94.

SCHAEFER, E. S., and BELL, R. Q. (1958) 'Development of a parental attitude research instrument'. *Child Devel.*, **29**, 339–61.

SCHAFFER, H. R. (1958) 'Objective observations of personality development in early infancy'. *Brit. J. Med. Psychol.*, **31**, 174–83.

SCHAFFER, H. R., and CALLENDER, W. M. (1959) 'Psychological effects of hospitalization in infancy'. *Pediatrics*, **24**, 528–39.

SCOTT, E. M., and THOMSON, A. M. (1956) 'A psychological investigation of primi gravidae. IV. Psychological factors and the clinical phenomena of labour'. *J. Obst. gynaecol. Brit. Emp.*, **63**, 502–8.

SCOTT, J. P., and MARSTON, M. (1950) 'Critical periods affecting the development of normal and maladjustive social behaviour of puppies'. *J. Genet. Psychol.*, **77**, 25-60.

SEARS, R. R., MACCOBY, E. E., and LEVIN, H. (1957) *Patterns of Child Rearing*. Evanston, Ill.: Row, Peterson.

SPITZ, R. A. (1946) 'The smiling response: a contribution to the ontogenesis of social relations'. *Genet. Psychol. Monogr.*, **34**, 57-125.

THOMPSON, W. R. (1955) 'Early environment – its importance for later behavior'. In P. H. Hoch and J. Zubin (Eds.) *Psychopathology of Childhood*. New York: Grune and Stratton.

THORPE, W. H. (1956) *Learning and Instinct in Animals*. London: Methuen.

THORPE, W. H. (1961) 'Sensitive periods in the learning of animals and men: a study of imprinting with special reference to the induction of cyclic behaviour'. In W. H. Thorpe and O. L. Zangwill (Eds.) *Current Problems in Animal Behaviour*. London: Cambridge U.P.

WHITE, B., and WOLFF, P. (1962) 'Interaction of visual pursuit and sucking in the newborn infant'. Unpublished.

WOLFF, P. (1959) 'Observations on newborn infants'. *Psychosomatic Med.*, **21**, 110-18.

Index

Accident proneness, 64
Activity, 53, 135
Adaptation level, 164
Affectional systems, 3, 20, 29
  (*see also* Infant-mother, Mother-infant)
Aggression
  in child, 64
  in monkey mother, 9, 24, 37
Ahrens, R., 208, 241
Ambivalence, stage, 5, 7
Ambrose, J. A., 210, 241
Anaesthetics, 62
Anxiety
  child, 103, 105, 224
  mother, 53, 56
Approach-withdrawal, 10, 11
  play, 14, 16, 19
Arousal states, 60, 117, 125, 135
  (*see also* Wakefulness)
Arsenian, J. M., 78, 241
Asphyxia, 58
Attachment
  criteria, 101f, 104, 109, 180f
  development, 107, 139, 179-99
  in Ganda, 75f, 80f, 93f
  specific, 108, 110, 182f, 197
    (*see also* Discrimination, Recognition)
  stage, 5, 6
  to mother monkey, 7
    (*see also* Infant-mother)
Attention, lack of, 57
Auditory feedback, 171, 177
  pursuit, 135-6
  stimulus for smiling, 117f

Baby-snatching, monkeys, 8
Bakwin, H., 203
Baldwin, A. L., 195, 241
Behaviour problems, 57, 64

Bell, R. Q., 57, 243
Bergman, P., 62, 241
Berlyne, D. E., 178, 194, 241
Bowlby, J., 101, 179, 241
Brackbill, Y., 207, 221, 241
Brain damage, minimal, 53f
  in monkeys, 61
Breast feeding, 98, 100, 104, 138
Breese, F. H., 241
Brodbeck, A. J., 203
Broken homes, 106-7

Caesarean section, 55
Callender, W. M., 180, 243
Care, amount of, 96f
  warmth, 95
Caretakers, number of, 73, 85f, 95, 107
Choreiformic activity, 57, 63-4
Clapping hands, 80, 82
  (*see also* Pat-a-cake)
Clinging, infant to infant, 20, 22-3
  to mother, 79, 83
Communication, monkey, 35f
Concentration, lack of, 57, 65
Conflict, 49
Contact with mother, 16f, 20, 29, 102, 110, 152, 195
Cooley, J. A., 172, 243
Cramond, W. A., 58, 63, 241
Crawling, 85f
Critical period, 201-25, 228f
Crying, 53-6, 75-6, 80f, 105-6, 116, 123, 127, 176, 193, 221

Darwin, C., 115, 241
Davids, A., 58, 241
Deprivation, monkey, 17f, 33
Devault, S., 241
Dijkstra, J., 57, 241

Discrimination, 231
  of mother, 80–1, 215 (*see also* Recognition)
Dominance, monkey, 30, 40, 43, 44
Doyle, G. A., 171

E.E.G., 60–1
Emerson, P., 179n
E.M.G., 61
Erikson, E. H., 140, 161–2, 241
Escalona, S. K., 62, 115, 241
Exploration, 39, 40, 78, 171–8, 194
  manual, 4
  oral, 4, 12, 21, 22
  visual, 4, 26, 47
Expressions, *see* Facial expressions
Extinction, experimental, 172, 176
Eye-to-eye contact, 122, 156

Face, hiding, 78
Facial expressions, monkey, 12–13, 35f
Family background, 140f
  (*see also* Religion)
Father, *see* Paternal behaviour
Fear, monkeys, 37, 49
  of strangers, 83, 103, 105, 109, 182f, 204f
Feeding, children, 72, 74, 85f, 151–3, 158–9
  monkeys, 42
  (*see also* Milk supply, Schedule feeding)
Foetal distress, 55
Following, of mother, 77, 82, 85f
  response, 228f
Forcipal extraction, 55
Freud, S., 236

Ganda, the, 67f
Géber, M., 107, 241–2
Gesell, A., 165
Goldfarb, W., 203
Gough, D., 46, 242
Grasping, 53
Gray, P. H., 203f, 228, 242
Greeting, 79–83

Grin, monkey, 6
Grooming, monkey, 6, 11, 17, 37–42, 48

Habituation, 210f
Handlin, O., 140, 242
Harlow, H. F., 78, 195, 236, 242
Hebb, D. O., 194, 242
Helson, H., 164
Henriquez y Pimentel, M. J. D., 59
Hinde, R. A., 35, 209, 242, 243
Hormones, 9
Hyperexcitability syndrome, 54f, 62
Hyperkinetic child, 54, 61, 64
Hypokinetic child, 54f
Hypotonia, 62

Imitation, 4–5
Imprinting, 202f, 227–39
Individual differences, 194
Infant-infant affectional system, 3, 13, 17, 20f, 28–9
  clinging, 20, 22–3
  interaction, 28–9
  (*see also* Play)
Infant monkey, behaviour to other mothers, 10–11
  recognition of mother, 23
Infant-mother affectional system, 3f, 29
  specificity of, 23
  (*see also* Attachment)
Infant-mother interaction, 67–112, 161
Insecurity, 84, 103, 105
Interaction, monkeys, 37
  (*see also* Infant-infant, Infant-mother, Mother-child, Mother-infant)
Irwin, O. C., 203
Isolation, social, 33

Jaynes, J., 231, 242
Jensen, G. D., 19, 242

Kaila, E., 203

Kalhorn, J., 241
Kibuka, K., 67n
Kuhlman, C., 46, 122, 133

Labour, prolonged, 58
Laughing, 126, 137
Learning, 125, 135–6, 223, 228f
Lenneberg, E., 123
Levin, H., 244
Levy, D. M., 109, 166, 242
Levy, R. J., 203
Lorenz, K., 202, 228–9, 242
Lowery, L. G., 203

Maccoby, E. E., 244
Manual exploration, 4
Marston, M., 244
Maternal affectional system, 3–29
  behaviour, monkey, 3f
    of unmothered-mothers, 24f
  skill, monkey, 48–9
Mead, M., 95,100, 242
Mental defect, monkey, 32–3
Mental health, 65, 111
Middlemore, M. P., 186, 242
Milk supply, adequacy, 74, 85f, 99, 105
Moltz, H., 207, 223, 242
Monkey behaviour, 3–49
  (*see also* Infant monkey)
  communication, 35f
Moro response, 54
Mother, attachment to, *see* Attachment, specific
  -child interaction, 53–66
  -infant interaction, 3–29, 37f, 161
  withdrawal, 24f
  responses to other infants, 9
  warmth of, 94
Motivation, 163–7

Negative responses to mother, 7
Neonates, 53f
Neurological examination of infant, 53, 59–60

Operant behaviour, 171f
  level, 172, 178
Oral exploration, 4, 12, 21–2
Overprotection, maternal, 53

Palmer, F. H., 232, 243
Para-natal complications, 53
Parental Attitude Research Instrument, 57
Pat-a-cake (*or* Patty-cake), 80, 125–7, 138
Paternal behaviour, monkey, 40, 42f, 48,
  human, 146f
Personality of mother, 56–8, 62–3
Piaget, J., 133, 160–3, 165, 180–1, 183, 243
Play, child, 103, 136
  monkey, 6, 9, 13–16, 19, 22, 41–2
Playpen situation, 3f
Playroom, 21
Polygamy, 72f, 111
Prechtl, H. F. R., 57, 243
Pregnancy, stress during, 58
Premature baby smiling, 116n, 117
Pre-natal complications, 53
Presenting, monkeys, 6, 31n, 41, 47
Psycho-analytic viewpoint, 235–9
Punishment, of infant monkey, 7, 26

Rat and infant compared, 175
Recognition of individual, 38, 41
  of mother, 23, 47
  (*see also* Discrimination)
Reinforcement, 19, 47, 106, 171f, 231
Rejection, maternal, 53
Religion of child's family, 72f, 85f, 111
Respiration, 60, 135
Rheingold, H., 172, 193, 196, 243
Richards, A. I., 67n
Roles, in infant monkeys, 22
Rooting response, 53
Rose, J. A., 65, 243
Rowell, T. E., 34, 242–3

Index

Schaefer, E. S., 57, 243
Schaffer, H. R., 180, 189, 243
Schedule feeding, 83, 98, 104, 106
Schizophrenia, 238
Scott, E. M., 58, 63, 243
Scott, J. P., 232, 244
Sears, R. R., 195, 244
Security, 84, 93f, 103–5
Sensitive period, 230
  (*see also* Critical period)
Separation, anxiety, 22, 103, 188
  at weaning, 67
  effects of, 75, 81
  of infant monkeys, 17–19, 48
  stage, 5, 8
  upset, as measure, 181
Sexual behaviour of monkeys, 30f
  of unmothered monkey mothers, 27f, 30
  precocity, 143
Sleep, 53, 115, 117f
Smiling, 53, 75, 76, 81, 86f, 113–38, 204f
  in prematures, 116–17
  in sleep, 117f, 128
  social, 119
  stimuli for, 117f
  while feeding, 128
Social attachment, *see* Attachment
  development, monkeys, 35f
  inadequacy, monkey, 12, 33
  isolation, 33
  play, 14
  playroom, 21
  responsiveness, 201f
Socio-economic background of parents, 62
Spitz, R. A., 33, 183, 203–4, 244
Stanley, W. C., 171–2, 243
Startle response, 54, 117, 135
Stemmer, C. J., 57, 243
Stimulation, need for, 192f
Stimulus, *see* Auditory, Visual
Stimulus hunger, 165, 194
Strangers, response to, 81–3, 105, 109
  (*see also* Fear)
Sucking, in human infants, 53–4

in humans and monkeys, 46–7
non-nutritional, 4
thumb, 21, 99, 100, 104, 221
Surrogate mothers, monkey, 11f, 21f

Talmadge, M., 241
Thompson, W. R., 194, 244
Thomson, A. M., 58, 63, 243
Thorpe, W. H., 222, 242, 244
Together-together infant monkeys, 20 f
Toilet training, 106
Tolman, C. W., 19, 242
Tonus, in infant, 53–5
Toxaemia, 55
Twins, 72, 90, 92, 106

Uterine dysfunction, 58–9

van der Gaag, 54
Vince, M. A., 242
Visual exploration, 4, 26, 27
  feedback, 171, 177
  fixation on infant, 18, 47
  fixation on mother, 17–18, 46, 138
  orientation to infant, 6
  pursuit, 121, 127
  responses, self-reinforcing, 19
  stimuli in smiling, 121f
Vocabulary, monkey, 35
Vocalization, 35f, 75–6, 81, 123, 129f
Vomiting, 150–1

Wakefulness, 53, 116
  (*see also* Arousal)
Weaning, responses to, 83
  separation at, 67
Weiss, P., 124, 133
Welbourn, H., 67n
Westrate, H. C., 59
White, B., 122, 162, 244
Windle, Dr, 61
Wolf, K. M., 203
Wolff, P., 115, 122, 244

Zimmermann, R. R., 242